Good Cheap Eats in London

Twelfth edition

Other Harden's titles

London Restaurants
UK Restaurant Guide
London Bars & Pubs
London for Free
Party, Conference & Event Guide

Sign up to be a restaurant critic?

Earn yourself a free copy of our next restaurant guide by completing our restaurant survey.

Register at hardens.com

© Harden's Limited 2009

ISBN 978-1-873721-88-9

British Library Cataloguing-in-Publication data:
a catalogue record for this book is available from
the British Library.

Printed and bound in Finland by WS Bookwell

Research Assistant: Rebecca Halfond
Production Assistant: Fiona Aranguren

Harden's Limited
14 Buckingham Street
London WC2N 6DF

CONTENTS

Ratings & prices

RATINGS & PRICES

RATINGS

Ratings are based both on our own experiences –
we have visited all of the listed establishments at our
own expense – and also on the views of the reporters
who take part in our annual survey. We have given
ratings as follows:

★★ Exceptional
London's top bargains. They offer a quality of
cooking which is, given the price, worth travelling for.

★ Very good
Places where the cooking offers above-average
value for money.

𝔸 Good atmosphere
Spots with particular "buzz", style or charm.

PRICES

So you can compare the costs of different
establishments, we have tried to give a realistic
estimate of the cost for a typical meal in each place.

For *restaurants, pubs and wine bars,* we have given an
estimate of the cost for one (1) person of two courses
with a drink and a cup of coffee.

For *cafés,* the price we show is the approximate cost
of a sandwich, a cake and a cup of coffee.

These prices include service (we have included a 10% tip
if there is no service charge), VAT and any cover charge.

* In the directory section, where an asterisk appears
next to the price, you can keep expenditure to £25 or
less only at certain times of day (usually lunch); by
sticking to a particular menu; or (in a few cases) by eating
in a specified area, such as the bar. Eating at other times
or from the à la carte menu may be much more
expensive – see the text of the entry for details.

(𝔸★) In the area overview indexes, where ratings appear
in brackets, the same provisos apply as when an asterisk
(*) is used in the directory section.

---

*Telephone number – all numbers should be prefixed with '020' if dialling
from outside the London area.*

*Map reference – shown immediately after the telephone number.
(Major coffee shop chains are not shown on the maps.)*

Website – if applicable, is the first entry in the small print.

*Last orders time – the first entry in the small print, after the website
(if applicable); Sunday may be up to 90 minutes earlier.*

*Opening hours – unless otherwise stated, restaurants are open for lunch and
dinner seven days a week.*

*Credit and debit cards – unless otherwise stated, Mastercard, Visa, Amex and
Switch are accepted.*

*Dress – where appropriate, the management's preferences concerning
patrons' dress are given.*

INTRODUCTION

This is the twelfth edition of our guide for anyone who wants to enjoy eating out in London while keeping costs under control. It is easier than many people might think to find interesting and satisfying meals at modest cost. And it's not even as if you are restricted to a particular *type* of establishment or particular areas. The coverage of this guide extends all the way from basic East End canteens to grand, 'big name' restaurants in the heart of fashionable London.

For this edition, we have imposed a cut-off point – the maximum price to qualify for inclusion in the guide – of £25 a head (very occasionally allowing ourselves a few pence leeway!). For this amount, a qualifying establishment must provide two courses, a drink, coffee and service. (If there is no compulsory service charge, we have allowed for a 10% tip.) Many of the places listed can in fact be visited – perhaps for light meals or snacks – for less than the 'formula' price we give.

Diners on a budget, in particular, have to know *where* to go, of course – but it's often almost more important to know *when*. Many of the more interesting experiences are to be had at places where the price is asterisked* – see the previous page for an explanation. These are usually 'proper' restaurants which experience a shortage of custom at lunchtime (or, in some office areas, dinner time). They offer low-price set menus as loss leaders, hoping either to make up the difference through wine sales or to impress customers enough to guarantee a return visit. Whatever the restaurateurs' motives, there are some great bargains to be had – especially for those who do not need too much wine with their meal!

We wish you some excellent eating out around town. Perhaps you would like to tell us about your successes (or any failures). Every spring, we conduct a detailed survey of restaurant-goers' experiences. Those who participate – some 8,000 people in 2008 – receive a complimentary copy of the resulting guide.

We invite you, too, to register to take part in the survey by visiting hardens.com. You will then be able to keep a 'diary' of your dining experiences. You can use this for your own reference, but it will also help you to take part in the survey.

Richard Harden   **Peter Harden**

RECOMMENDATIONS

BEST FOOD ★★

For £15 & under:

Alisan (HA9)
Brick Lane Beigel Bake (E1)
Franco Manca (SW9)
Fuzzy's Grub (Group)
Golden Hind (W1)
Hot Stuff (SW8)
Jashan (HA0)
Jenny Lo's Tea House (SW1)
Lahore Kebab House (E1)
Lisboa Patisserie (W10)
Lovage (SE1)

Mandalay (W2)
Mangal (E8)
Mirch Masala (chain)
Monmouth Coffee Co. (SE1)
New Tayyabs (E1)
Sagar (Group)
The Sea Cow (SE22)
Sree Krishna (SW17)
Tosa (W6)
El Vergel (SE1)

For £15-£25

Amaranth (SW18)
Anchor & Hope (SE1)
Anglesea Arms (W6)
Arbutus (W1)
Arch One (SE1)
Babur Brasserie (SE23)
Back to Basics (W1)
Barrafina (W1)
Beirut Express (Group)
Bocca Di Lupo (W1)
Chez Marcelle (W14)
Dehesa (W1)
Dinings (W1)
Edokko (WC1)
Esarn Kheaw (W12)
Faro (E14)
Faulkner's (E8)
Fish Club (SW11)
Fish Hook (W4)
Galvin at Windows (W1)
Galvin Bistro de Luxe (W1)
Geeta (NW6)
Hilliard (EC4)
Inaho (W2)
Indian Zing (W6)
Jin Kichi (NW3)
Kastoori (SW17)
Koba (W1)

Ma Cuisine (Group)
Madhu's (UB1)
Mandarin Kitchen (W2)
Mango & Silk (SW14)
Min Jiang (W8)
Mohsen (W14)
Moro (EC1)
Paddyfield (SW12)
Passage Cafe (EC1)
Patara (Group)
Pham Sushie (EC1)
Philpotts Mezzaluna (NW2)
Pizza Metro (SW11)
Rasa (N16)
Rasa (Group)
Salt Yard (W1)
Sông Quê (E2)
St John Bread & Wine (E1)
Taiwan Village (SW6)
Tentazioni (SE1)
Terroirs (WC2)
Vijay (NW6)
Yauatcha (W1)
Yming (W1)

RECOMMENDATIONS

BEST ALL-ROUND DEALS Ⓐ★★

Amaranth *(SW18)*

Babur Brasserie *(SE23)*

Barrafina *(W1)*

Bocca di Lupo *(W1)*

Dehesa *(W1)*

Eddoko *(WC1)*

Galvin at Windows *(W1)*

Galvin Bistro de Luxe *(W1)*

Hilliard *(EC4)*

Hot Stuff *(SW8)*

Indian Zing *(W6)*

Koba *(W1)*

Min Jiang *(W8)*

Monmouth Coffee Co. *(SE1)*

Moro *(EC1)*

Philpott's Mezzaluna *(NW2)*

Pizza Metro *(SW11)*

MOST INTERESTING 'ETHNIC' PLACES

Alisan *(HA9)*

Amaranth *(SW18)*

Babur Brasserie *(SE23)*

Beirut Express *(Group)*

Chez Liline *(N4)*

Dinings *(W1)*

Edokko *(WC1)*

Esarn Kheaw *(W12)*

Geeta *(NW6)*

Hot Stuff *(W8)*

Inaho *(W2)*

Indian Zing *(W6)*

Jashan *(HA0)*

Jenny Lo's Tea House *(SW1)*

Jin Kichi *(NW3)*

Kastoori *(SW17)*

Koba *(W1)*

Lahore Kebab House *(E1)*

Madhu's *(UB1)*

Mandalay *(W2)*

Mandarin Kitchen *(W2)*

Mangal *(E8)*

Mango & Silk *(SW14)*

Mirch Masala *(Group)*

Mohsen *(W14)*

New Tayyabs *(E1)*

Paddyfield *(SW12)*

Pham Sushie *(EC1)*

Rasa *(N16)*

Rasa *(Group)*

Sagar *(Group)*

Sree Krishna *(SW17)*

Sông Quê *(E2)*

Taiwan Village *(SW6)*

Tosa *(W6)*

El Vergel *(SE1)*

Vijay *(NW6)*

Yauatcha *(W1)*

Yming *(W1)*

BEST NON-ETHNIC NOSH

Anchor & Hope *(SE1)*

Anglesea Arms *(W6)*

Arbutus *(W1)*

Arch One *(SE1)*

Back to Basics *(W1)*

Bull & Last *(NW5)*

Fish Hook *(W4)*

Fuzzy's Grub *(Group)*

Galvin at Windows *(W1)*

Galvin Bistro de Luxe *(W1)*

Hilliard *(EC4)*

Ma Cuisine *(Group)*

The Passage Cafe *(EC1)*

St John Bread & Wine *(E1)*

Terroirs *(WC2)*

THE MOST STYLISH PLACES

Babur Brasserie *(SE23)*
Barrafina *(W1)*
Bocca Di Lupo *(W1)*
Brompton Bar & Grill *(SW7)*
Busaba Eathai *(Group)*
Le Cercle *(SW1)*
Cha Cha Moon *(W1)*
Clos Maggiore *(WC2)*
Le Colombier *(SW3)*
Dehesa *(W1)*
Eight Over Eight *(SW3)*
The Forge *(WC2)*
Frederick's *(N1)*

Galvin at Windows *(W1)*
Galvin Bistro de Luxe *(W1)*
Inamo *(W1)*
Moro *(EC1)*
Pearl Liang *(W2)*
Pellicci's *(E2)*
Pont de la Tour Bar & Grill *(SE1)*
Princi *(W1)*
St Alban *(W1)*
Tartine *(SW3)*
Tate Modern *(SE1)*
The Wolseley *(W1)*

BEST FOR ROMANCE

Arancia *(SE16)*
Babur Brasserie *(SE23)*
Blue Elephant *(SW6)*
La Bouchée *(SW7)*
Brompton Bar & Grill *(SW3)*
Brula *(TW1)*
Café Laville *(W2)*
La Cage Imaginaire *(NW3)*
Le Cercle *(SW1)*
Clos Maggiore *(WC2)*
Le Colombier *(SW3)*
Eight Over Eight *(SW3)*
The Forge *(WC2)*
Frederick's *(N1)*

Galvin at Windows *(W1)*
Glaisters *(SW10)*
Gordon's Wine Bar *(WC2)*
Le Mercury *(N1)*
Mon Plaisir *(WC2)*
Osteria Basilico *(W11)*
Patio *(W12)*
Pearl Liang *(W2)*
Polish Club *(SW7)*
La Trouvaille *(WC2)*
Villa Bianca *(NW3)*
Windsor Castle *(W8)*
Wódka *(W8)*
The Wolseley *(W1)*

BEST BREAKFAST/BRUNCH

The Albion *(E2)*
Apostrophe *(Group)*
Banners *(N8)*
Boiled Egg & Soldiers *(SW11)*
The Brew House *(NW3)*
Café Laville *(W2)*
Café Mozart *(N6)*
Chamomile *(NW3)*
Chelsea Bun Diner *(SW10)*
Cock Tavern *(EC1)*
Del'Aziz *(Group)*
Deptford Project *(SE8)*
Fuzzy's Grub *(Group)*
Gail's Bread *(Group)*
Kensington Square Kitchen *(W8)*

Lucky Seven *(W11)*
Maison Bertaux *(W1)*
Mona Lisa *(SW10)*
Monmouth Coffee Company *(Group)*
E Pellicci *(E2)*
St John Bread & Wine *(E1)*
Smiths of Smithfield *(EC1)*
Star Café *(W1)*
Table *(SE1)*
Tapa Room *(W1)*
Tom's *(W11)*
Troubadour *(SW5)*
The Wolseley *(W1)*

RECOMMENDATIONS

TOP PUB GRUB

Anchor & Hope *(SE1)*
Anglesea Arms *(W6)*
The Atlas *(SW6)*
The Barnsbury *(N1)*
The Bull & Last *(NW5)*
The Charles Lamb *(N1)*
The Churchill Arms *(W8)*
The Cock Tavern *(EC1)*
The Cow *(W2)*
The Cumberland Arms *(W14)*
The Duke's Head *(SW15)*
The Eagle *(EC1)*
The Fox *(EC2)*
The Gowlett Arms *(SE15)*
The Hartley *(E1)*
The Lansdowne *(NW1)*
The Norfolk Arms *(WC1)*

The Normanby *(SW15)*
Old Parr's Head *(W14)*
The Palmerston *(SE22)*
The Princess Victoria *(W12)*
The Queen's Head *(W6)*
The Running Horse *(W1)*
The Rye *(SE15)*
The Ship *(SW18)*
Somerstown Coffee
   House *(NW1)*
The Thatched House *(W6)*
The Walmer Castle *(W11)*
The White Horse *(SW6)*
The William IV *(NW10)*
The Windsor Castle *(W8)*

THE BEST FUN PLACES

Aglio e Olio *(SW10)*
The Albion *(E2)*
The Atlas *(SW6)*
L'Artista *(NW11)*
Barrafina *(W1)*
Blue Elephant *(SW6)*
Bordello *(E1)*
La Bouchée *(SW7)*
Buona Sera *(SW3)*
Le Cercle *(SW1)*
Cha Cha Moon *(Group)*
Chakalaka *(SW15)*
The Charles Lamb *(N1)*
The Churchill Arms *(W8)*
Ciao Bella *(WC1)*
The Cow *(W2)*
Crazy Homies *(W2)*
Dehesa *(W1)*
The Drunken Monkey *(E1)*
Eagle Bar Diner *(W1)*
Eight Over Eight *(SW3)*
El Rincón Latino *(SW4)*
Electric Birdcage *(W1)*
Fish in a Tie *W1*
Gallipoli *(Group)*
Gordon's Wine Bar *(WC2)*
Inamo *(W1)*
The Lansdowne *(NW1)*
Lemonia *(NW1)*

Little Bay *(Group)*
Lola Rojo *(SW11)*
Lucky Seven *(W11)*
Le Mercury *(N1)*
Meson don Felipe *(SE1)*
Moro *(EC1)*
Osteria Basilico *(W11)*
Pagliaccio *(SW6)*
Pappa e Ciccia *(Group)*
The Patio *(W12)*
Pearl Liang *(W2)*
Pizza Metro *(SW11)*
Pizza On The Park *(SW1)*
Rebato's *(SW8)*
Riccardo's *(SW3)*
Rocket *(Group)*
Rye *(SE15)*
Shampers *(W1)*
Shanghai *(E8)*
The Ship *(SW18)*
Simpson's Tavern *(EC3)*
Sitaaray *(WC2)*
Smiths of Smithfield *(EC1)*
Story Deli (The Old
   Truman Brewery) *(E1)*
Taqueria *(W11)*
Village East *(SE1)*
Walmer Castle *(W11)*

DIRECTORY

Abeno WC1 £20 A★
47 Museum St 7405 3211 2–1C
This friendly Japanese outfit, near the British Museum (and now with a Theatreland offshoot) offers very reasonable set lunch menus (£8.80-£12.80). The speciality is okonomi-yaki – a cross between a pancake and an omelette, cooked at your table. At à la carte prices, and with house wine at £13.95 a bottle, you'd need to take some care to stay within our price limit. / www.abeno.co.uk; 10 pm.

Abokado WC2 £11 ★
160 Drury Ln 7242 5600 4–2D
This small healthy-eating chain is a reliable stand-by for those in search of a good-quality snack meal – perhaps the likes of a chicken & avocado wrap (£2.89) and a smoothie (£3.39). Or go for one of the hot Oriental-style dishes, such as noodles or dumpling soup, which generally come in at less than a fiver. / www.abokado.com; 7.30 pm; closed Sat & Sun.

Abu Zaad W12 £13 A★
29 Uxbridge Rd 8749 5107 7–1C
By Shepherd's Bush Market, a Middle Eastern café/takeaway with little obvious to distinguish it from its local peers. It's well worth truffling out, though, thanks to its genuine Syrian mezze and kebabs, all at easy-to-afford prices. Moussaka is just £3, while a shish taouk (chicken kebab in a 'special sauce') will set you back £7.50. Another saving: there's no alcohol! To dine in (somewhat) greater grandeur, seek out the 'Aladdin's Cave' section, to the rear. / www.abuzaad.co.uk; 11 pm.

Adams Café W12 £20 A★
77 Askew Rd 8743 0572 7–1B
This friendly Shepherd's Bush spot is a popular oddity – by day a greasy spoon, and by night well-known for its Tunisian and Moroccan specialities. Prix-fixe menus, which all include complimentary appetisers and mint tea or coffee, include a 1-course "rapide" (£11.50) and a 2-course "gourmet" (£14.50). Your choice for the latter might be 'brik au thon' – crispy filo filled with tuna, egg & fresh herbs – followed by a lamb couscous. Save a couple of pounds for a shot of Tunisian digestif, made from figs. BYO (corkage £3). / 11 pm; closed Sun.

Addie's Thai Café SW5 £18 A★
121 Earl's Court Rd 7259 2620 5–2A
One of the better options for food near Earl's Court tube, this Oriental café offers friendly service, and good-value grub. With main courses around £6 and house wine at £12.50 a bottle, it slips easily under our price limit at any time. / www.addiesthai.co.uk; 11 pm; closed Sat L & Sun L; no Amex.

Afghan Kitchen N1 £16 ★
35 Islington Grn 7359 8019 8–3D
It offers little in the way of creature comforts, but if you're looking for cooking that's unusual, as well as filling and good value, you won't do much better than this tiny café, overlooking Islington Green. There are eight main dishes on offer – four meat (£6.50 a piece), and four veg (around £5). All are served in portions to satisfy the hungriest punter. Rice or a large chunk of bread add £3.50 to the cost, washed down with house wine at £15 a bottle. / 11 pm; closed Mon & Sun; no credit cards.

Aglio e Olio SW10   £20   A★

194 Fulham Rd   7351 0070   5–3B

*This fun and noisy Italian café is just the job if you find yourself
needing to eat in the vicinity of the Chelsea and Westminster
Hospital. The pasta is excellent and extremely affordable – fusilli with
meatballs & herbs, for instance, comes in at £8.90. Rounding the
meal off with a panna cotta will set you back a further £4.50.
A bottle of the house vino is £12.90. / 11.30 pm.*

Al-Waha W2   £23

75 Westbourne Grove   7229 0806   6–1B

*This small and unassuming Bayswater café is one of London's better
Lebanese restaurants. With reasonable care you could eat here
at any time within our budget by making a meal from the mezze,
most of which are £5 or £6. For the hungry, the £14 lunchtime
specials (till 5pm) – which will give you a mezze platter (hummus,
moutable, tabbouleh), plus a shish taouk or shish kafta – is especially
worth seeking out. House wine is £13.50 a bottle.
/ www.alwaharestaurant.com; 11.30 pm; no Amex.*

Alba EC1   £24*   ★

107 Whitecross St   7588 1798   9–1B

*This low-key Italian – specialising in Piedmontese cuisine – has been
one of the few bright sparks around the Barbican for nearly 20 years
now. Generally, it's well out of our price-range, but – here on the
fringes of the City – a set-price dinner menu (£15.50) is offered that's
especially worth seeking out. This might comprise smoked duck
breast, then grilled calves liver with spinach & potatoes and –
if you're prepared to blow another £2.50 – the cake of the day
to finish. The wine list offers a lot of interest to lovers of Italian wine,
with glasses from £3.75. / www.albarestaurant.com; 11 pm; closed
Sat & Sun.*

Albion E2   £22   A★

2-4 Boundary St   7729 1051   9–1D

*Sir Terence Conran recently opened this smart English café/bistro
on the edge of fashionable Shoreditch. They do their own baking,
and if you want a proper 'bloomer' (£2 to take away), we doubt you'll
do better than here. Accordingly, 'doorstop' sandwiches (around
£4.25) are something of a highlight, and the bread 'n' butter pudding
& custard (£5) is pretty good too. With wines kicking off at £2.75
a glass, however, our budget will also run to the meatier items on the
menu – a rib-eye steak, for example, is £8.50. / www.albioncaff.co.uk.*

Ali Baba NW1   £10   ★

32 Ivor Pl   7723 5805   2–1A

*You'll feel you've made a 'find' when you enter this offbeat café,
behind a takeaway, near Marylebone Station – it seemingly doubles
up as its proprietors, the Ali family's living room, and you'll often find
al Jazeera blaring away on the TV. The ethos is 'take us as you find
us'. What you'll probably find is some excellent and very cheap
Egyptian dishes – tabbouleh salad is £3.50, for example,
and amongst heartier dishes cabsa (red rice & lamb) is £6. BYO.
/ midnight; no credit cards.*

Alisan HA9 £15 ★★

The Junction, Engineers Way, Wembley 8903 3888 1–1A
*You wouldn't typically travel to Wembley for anything other than
curry, but this ambitious modern Chinese, right by the stadium, is well
worth seeking out too. Dim sum is a menu feature all day,
with most dishes costing £3-£4, and can be mixed with more
substantial Cantonese food (typically £8). A bottle of house wine
is £12.90, or there's a range of bottled beers for about £3.
/ www.alisan.co.uk; Mon-Thu 11 pm, Fri & Sat 11.30 pm, Sun 10.30 pm.*

The Almeida N1 £23* ★

30 Almeida St 7354 4777 8–2D
*D&D London (formerly 'Conran') restaurants are generally too
upmarket for this guide. The group's sole north London property –
near the eponymous Islington theatre – is an exception, offering a 2-
course 'Menu du Jour' at lunch or pre-theatre – you might find the
likes of pork rillettes, followed by duck breast in peppercorn sauce.
For another £3 you could have lemon & raspberry posset to finish.
House wine isn't too pricey either, considering, at £14.50 a bottle
(or £3.50 a glass). / www.almeida-restaurant.co.uk; 10.30pm, Sun 9pm.*

Alounak £17 ★

10 Russell Gdns, W14 7603 1130 7–1D
44 Westbourne Grove, W2 7229 0416 6–1B
*The days are long gone since the original Alounak – a kebab stop in a
Portakabin by the Olympia train tracks. Nowadays these BYO
(no corkage) spots occupy a cheap 'n' cheerful café around the
corner from the first site, plus a similarly functional branch
in Bayswater. For a no-frills supper on a budget they're ideal,
with freshly-baked flat breads to accompany mezze (from £2.90) and
good kebabs (from £6.50). / 11.30 pm; no Amex.*

Amano £16 ★

20 Sumner St, SE1 7234 9530 9–4B
More London Pl, (off Weavers Lane), SE1 7407 9751 9–4D
Potters Field, SE1 7407 9759 9–4D
Victor Wharf, Clink St, SE1 7234 0000 9–3C
*An emerging force on the ever-trendier South Bank, this chic mini-
chain provides a handy handful of bar/diner outlets. They are open all
hours, and all change their wide-ranging 'offers' as the day
progresses. Their Mediterranean-influenced 'offers' are hard
to summarise, but let's just say that there are few meals they can't
cater for, and for full details you'll have to see the catchy website.
House wine is £12.95 a bottle. / www.amanocafe.com.*

Amaranth SW18 £18 Ⓐ★★

346 Garratt Ln 8874 9036 10–2B
*It's not just dearth of competition down Earlsfield way that's made
this basic Thai café such a local phenomenon – this crammed
Oriental is the epitome of an efficient and friendly local institution.
Assisted by the BYO policy, it's also an extremely affordable one.
A classic dish like green chicken curry is £6.95, perhaps with prawns
in a blanket (£4.95) beforehand. Make sure you book! / 10.30 pm;
D only, closed Sun; no Amex.*

Amato W1 £18

14 Old Compton St   7734 5733   4–2A

This 'Caffè Pasticceria' is nowadays under the same ownership as the Richoux chain of French café/pâtisseries, and cakes (around £3.50) are the main deal. There are also snacks such as the un-Italian-sounding croque monsieur (around £4), as well as a wide selection of pasta dishes from about £8. The caffè is licensed (wine is £13.95 a bottle), but hot chocolate & whipped cream (£2.80) is the way to go. / www.amato.co.uk; Mon-Sat 10 pm, Sun 8 pm; no booking.

Ambassador EC1 £18

55 Exmouth Mkt   7837 0009   9–1A

An Exmouth Market two-year-old which delivers an unpretentious and reliable menu of seasonal food at good-value prices. Value is best at lunch and pre-theatre, when there's a 2-course deal for £12.50 (3-course, £16). A typical selection would be butternut squash soup, then moules marinière (and pear crumble if you go the whole hog). Wine is a key part of the formula, and the interesting selection starts at £14.50 a bottle. / www.theambassadorcafe.co.uk; 10.15 pm; closed Sun D.

The Anchor & Hope SE1 £24   ★★

36 The Cut   7928 9898   9–4A

Arrive early or expect to be drunk by the time you get a table (no booking, except for Sunday lunch) at this madly busy Waterloo boozer, renowned for its earthy British cooking. You'll need to take some care to stick to our budget, but it's not too tricky – you might have griddled ox hearts (£5) followed by black face haggis with neeps (£24 for two people). Wine starts at £2 for a small glass, or a pint of Bombardier will set you back £3. / 10.30 pm; closed Mon L & Sun D; no Amex; no booking.

The Anglesea Arms W6 £24   ★★

35 Wingate Rd   8749 1291   7–1B

You could easily breach our budget at this lovely pub, near Ravenscourt Park. It would seem a shame, though, to exclude one of the best and most characterful gastropubs in town – if you had the likes of braised ox cheeks (£11.25) followed by chocolate marquis with pistachio praline and orange & mint salad (£5.25) – you could just about stick within it. A small but interesting selection of wine starts at £14 a bottle, or drink London Pride at £3.30 a pint. / Tue-Sat 10.30 pm, Sun & Mon 10 pm; no Amex; no booking.

Apostrophe £ 7   ★

16 Regent St, SW1   7930 9922   3–3D
10 Grosvenor St, W1   7499 6511   3–2B
216 Tott' Ct Rd, W1   7436 6688   2–1C
23 Barrett St, W1   7355 1001   3–1A
40-41 Great Castle St, W1   7637 5700   3–1C
215 Strand, WC2   7427 9890   4–2D
42 Gt Eastern St, EC2   7739 8412   9–1D
3-5 St Bride St, EC4   7353 3704   9–2A

This is mainly a take-away chain, but – as good Gallic-style pâtisseries are still surprisingly difficult to find – we still think it's well worth bringing to your attention, not least as a good place for a breakfast croissant (£1.30) and a good latte (£2.25). Sandwiches include the likes of the Paris (avocado, rocket, tomato, mayo, Parmesan, £4.45), and the Colmar (salami, rocket, mayo and chilli jam, £4.25). / www.apostropheuk.com; L & afternoon tea only, Barrett St 8pm; no Amex; no booking.

Arancia SE16   £24   Ⓐ

52 Southwark Park Rd   7394 1751   11–2A

*This brave little Italian bistro has long been a shining beacon
of hospitality in the perennially dim Bermondsey dining scene. It's
always been a keenly-priced destination à la carte, and they also offer
a 2-course set menu for £13.50, which brings prices down further.
Soup of the day with bruschetta is a typical starter, followed by daily-
changing specials such as orrecchiette with spicy sausage sauce.
Prices on the small, well-chosen Italian wine list start from £12.95
a bottle. / www.arancia-london.co.uk; 11 pm; closed Mon & Sun D.*

Arbutus W1   £25*   ★★

63-64 Frith St   7734 4545   4–2A

*A foodie smash hit of recent years, Anthony Demetre and Will Smith's
Soho bistro rather pioneered the current wave for quality-and-value
destinations in the heart of town, and the hearty Gallic cooking
continues to inspire rave reviews. You can enjoy a 3-course lunch for
just £15.50 – your choice might be beef tartare, roast rabbit & sweet
potato purée, finished off with an île flottante. The innovative wine
list – fifty vintages all available by the 250ml carafe – is a major
feature, but the house selection is a modest £12.50 a bottle.
/ www.arbutusrestaurant.co.uk; 10.45pm, Sun 9.30 pm.*

Arch One SE1   £18*   ★★

1 Mepham St   7401 2329   9–4A

*A Gordon Ramsay protégée is now chef at this cavernous
bar/restaurant by Waterloo station – if you want to get a taste
of what the Sweary One's cooking is all about, this is probably the
best opportunity you'll find to do so 'on the cheap'. By choosing
carefully, you can eat here within our budget at any time,
but best value is the set weekday lunch menu, which offers three
courses and a glass of wine for £12.90. This is 'proper' food too –
your meal might be duck terrine with fig & orange, followed by brill
poached in red wine with leek mash, and a crumble to finish.
/ www.arch-1.com.*

L'Artista NW11   £17

917 Finchley Rd   8731 7501   1–1B

*Underneath railway arches by the tube, this dated but fun Italian
is one of Golders Green's key spots for budget get-togethers of one
kind or another (beware: if anyone's having a birthday it can
be deafening!). The stodgy fare isn't very 'modern', but is certainly
filling and not too expensive, with a large range of pizzas available
from £5.20-£8.20. House wine at £11.90 bottle doesn't bump costs
up either. / 11.30 pm.*

The Atlas SW6   £22   Ⓐ★

16 Seagrave Rd   7385 9129   5–3A

*This characterful pub comes as a bit of a surprise, in a backstreet
behind Earl's Court II. Like many of the better gastropubs, it can
stretch our price limit, but it's worth seeking out for the high quality
of its food. There's a Mediterranean theme, so you might have
a main course of seafood risotto (£10) before a British staple dessert,
such as marmalade bread 'n' butter pudding (£5). House wine
is £12.50 a bottle, or drink a pint of London Pride for £3.10.
/ www.theatlaspub.co.uk; 10.30 pm; closed Sun D; no booking.*

Azou W6 £21

375 King St 8563 7266 7–2B

It's not quite the casbah, but this small restaurant on the fringes of Hammersmith is a cheerful little local, decked out in low budget souk style. A friendly owner dispenses tasty North African fare at prices that don't raise the blood pressure: a dish such as brik (pastry filled with tuna & egg) is £4.90, or a tajine romanne (a stew with chicken in a pomegranate sauce) is £8.50. House wine is £11.80 a bottle. / www.azou.co.uk; 11 pm; closed Sat L & Sun L; no Amex.

Babur Brasserie SE23 £24* A★★

119 Brockley Rise 8291 2400 1–4D

We've always been big fans of this inviting-looking Honor Oak Park Indian – its fame belies its somewhat obscure location, and it's well worth discovering if you find yourself down Lewisham way. The prices on the à la carte menu bring it almost outside our budget, but choosing carefully you can have items such as multani soole (£5.95) and masala dosa (£10.25) and stay just under. Wines kick off at £13.50 a bottle. / www.babur.info; 11.30 pm.

Back to Basics W1 £18* ★★

21a Foley St 7436 2181 2–1B

This small, cramped Fitzrovia bistro is one of the best places in the West End for spanking fresh fish, and the 2-course set lunch (£10) brings it within our price limit – you might have cream of broccoli soup followed up by fillet of seabass with lentils & roast peppers, washed down with wine at £14.95 a bottle. NB In summer, you'll need to arrive early to nab one of the small number of outside tables. / www.backtobasics.uk.com; 10.30 pm; closed Sun.

Balfour WC1 £20 ★

75-77 Marchmont St 7713 6111 8–4C

One of the smarter joints in Bloomsbury's tourist/student-land, this newish corner bistro is rather oddly-named, given that the menu is largely Italian. Its notably reasonable prices, however, make it a handy destination to know about at any time of day – most main courses weigh in at a tenner or less, and a rib-eye & fries is only £11.95. The daily-changing 2-course set lunch menu is just £6.95. Wines kick off at £2.95 a glass.

The Banana Leaf Canteen SW11 £15

75-79 Battersea Rise 7228 2828 10–2C

There's often a queue at busy times for access to this noisy Thai canteen in Battersea. You can eat here at any time within our budget, but for top value, visit at lunch or on a weekday evening (6pm-7pm), when starters are £2.75, and noodle dishes and curries are £4.95. Drinks aren't pricey either: a bottle of house wine is £10.95, or a Tiger beer £3.15. / 11 pm; need 6+ to book.

Bangalore Express SE1 £19 A★

103-107 Waterloo Rd 7021 0886 9–4A

Just by Waterloo Station, this spin-off from Chelsea's esteemed Painted Heron offers a very flexible menu of cheap and flavour-packed Indian dishes (£4-8), in surprisingly chic surroundings. It also has a full bar serving Cobra (£3.75 for a pint) and house wine for £13 a bottle (and a happy hour too, from 2.30pm-5.30pm). / www.bangaloreexpress.co.uk.

sign up for the survey at hardens.com

Bangkok SW7 £23 ★

9 Bute St 7584 8529 5–2B

Nothing much changes at this South Kensington stalwart, which opened in 1967, and is the UK's longest-established Thai restaurant. The food is a bit westernised, but the dishes invariably taste fresh, and prices – not least for this particular postcode – are reasonable: a satay is £5.75, and Thai green curry is £8.70. Beware wine prices, though – even the house selection is £14.50 a bottle. / 10.45 pm; closed Sun; no Amex.

Banners N8 £23

21 Park Rd 8348 2930 1–1C

It's as an atmospheric weekend venue for all the family that this funky Crouch End bar/diner is best known, so brunch (£6.95) is a natural forte (and the 2-course set weekday lunch at the same price, is worth checking out too). A la carte, starters (perhaps Thai prawn cakes or calamari) are around £5.75, and main courses (such as Jamaican jerk chicken or tuna steak) around £10.95. The house wine is £13.75 a bottle. / 11.30 pm, Fri midnight; no Amex.

Bar Italia W1 £10 Ⓐ

22 Frith St 7437 4520 4–2A

A cult venue for Soho trendies, this very Italian coffee bar of long standing – open 24 hours a day and non-stop at weekends – is the quintessential post-clubbing hang-out. Though the food is not the main event, options run to the likes of sandwiches and light pasta dishes (around the £5 mark). You can have a drink if you want to – house wine is a punishing £19.50 a bottle but an espresso (£2) remains the hipster's choice. / open 24 hours, Sun 3 am; no booking.

Bar Trattoria Semplice W1 £17*

22-23 Woodstock St 7491 8638 3–2B

We were frankly a bit disappointed with our initial visit to this understated new bar/trattoria (think Italian gastropub) offshoot of celebrated Mayfair restaurant Semplice. We'd like to think we were unlucky, though, and – just off the top end of pricey Bond Street – it's difficult to believe that its 2-course set lunch including a glass of house wine and a cup of coffee (£14.50) isn't worth knowing about. You could eat here within our price limit at other times too, but only with some care. / www.bartrattoriasemplice.com.

The Barnsbury N1 £15*

209-211 Liverpool Rd 7607 5519 8–2D

This civilised north-Islington gastropub is a great neighbourhood place, with a lovely walled garden and accommodating staff. It's not too pricey either, especially at weekday lunches, when simple dishes are offered in the £4-£8.50 range. To stay comfortably within our budget at dinner, you'd have to stick to the veggie main courses such as risotto (around a tenner) and a pudding (£5). House wine is £13.50 a bottle. / www.thebarnsbury.co.uk; 10 pm.

Barrafina W1 £24* Ⓐ★★

54 Frith St 7813 8016 4–2A

Sam and Eddie Hart's genius tapas bar – in homage to Barcelona's famous 'Cal Pep' – is one of London's foodie fave raves, and, as there are no bookings, you need to arrive early to bag one of the 23 perches at the bar. Some caution is necessary to stay within budget, but if you stick to less expensive wine (from £15 a bottle) and cheaper dishes (classic tortilla £4; Santiago tart £4) you can squeeze a meal just under our price limit. / www.barrafina.co.uk; 11 pm; closed Sun; no booking.

Bedford & Strand WC2 £22
1a Bedford St 7836 3033 4–4D
Despite its notable wine (starting at £13.25 a bottle), this newish 'bar – wine room – bistro' just off the Strand got off to a slow start foodwise. Things have picked up over time, however, and for a quality retreat from the hurly-burly of the West End, it's got a lot going for it. A la carte you might bust our price limit, but the all-day 'deli counter' menu has simple dishes like pâté for £6, and cheese or charcuterie boards to share for a tenner. / www.bedford-strand.com; 11 pm; closed Sat L & Sun.

Bedlington Café W4 £16
24 Fauconberg Rd 8994 1965 7–2A
This long-established Chiswick dive – an ex greasy joe, turned Thai caff – was once, arguably, London's top cheap eat. It's no longer worth crossing town for, but still offers reliable Oriental dishes, with most main courses between £4.50-£12.50. Unlike in its heyday it's now licensed (with house wine at £13), but you can still BYO (£1 corkage). / 10 pm; closed Sun L; no credit cards.

Beirut Express £22 ★★
65 Old Brompton Rd, SW7 7591 0123 5–2B
112-114 Edgware Rd, W2 7724 2700 6–1D
You have to admire the Maroush Group and its ever-expanding empire, which includes the Ranoush chain and this duo of Lebanese fast food cafés. A visit to the Edgware Road original (in particular) gives you the experience of a journey to the Middle East at about the same price as a visit to PizzaExpress. There's a wide range of mezze priced about £4.50, with a mixed platter coming in at £10. Opt for the kebabs and other main dishes and you'll bust the budget. There's no alcohol, but a wonderfully tempting array of fresh juices at about £1.85. / W2 2am, SW7 midnight; W2 no credit cards.

Bento NW1 £14
9 Parkway 7482 3990 8–3B
A simple Japanese café, that's ideal for a swift bite in Camden Town. A range of bento boxes are served all day (costing from £8-£10.50), and are even cheaper at lunch. House wine is £11.50 a bottle. / bentocafe.co.uk; 10.15, Fri & Sat 10.45.

Best Mangal W14 £18 Ⓐ★
104 North End Rd 7610 1050 7–2D
In the thin area near West Kensington tube, this duo of Turkish BBQs make an excellent discovery. There's a range of mezze (£2.75-£7.75), but the highpoint are the quality kebabs (£8.50-£12) cooked at a central charcoal grill. A bottle of house wine is £13.75 or try Efes beer for £2.85. / midnight; no Amex.

Beyoglu NW3 £17 ★
72 Belsize Ln 7435 7733 8–2A
A simple Turkish restaurant in Belsize Park which won't break the bank at any time, but especially if you go for its lunchtime deal that offers two courses and coffee for £8.99 – the main dish will be something like grilled lamb steak. House wine is £14.90 a bottle. / www.beyoglu.co.uk; 11 pm; no Amex or Maestro.

Bistro I   **£15**

27 Frith St, W1   7734 6204   4–3A
75 Beak St, W1   7287 1840   3–2D
33 Southampton St, WC2   7379 7585   4–3D

Central London is remarkably short of straight-down-the-line, Central Castings-perfect budget bistros. While no one would single out this small chain for its stellar cuisine, it fills this rôle very well, and – as it's all prix-fixe – you can be certain how much you're going to spend too. Three courses will set you back £10.90 at dinner (£7.90 at lunch) – your meal might be smoked duck salad, followed by penne chicken arrabbiata, and cheesecake. House wine is £10.50 a bottle.
/ www.bistro1.co.uk; 11.30 pm.

Blue Elephant SW6   **£23***   A★

4-6 Fulham Broadway   7385 6595   5–4A

You won't find anywhere in this guide more lavish than this Fulham theme palace, with its jungle, streams (complete with fish) and bridges. By night, it's a big-budget date and party place, but if the target of your affections is available in the middle of the day, you can enjoy much of the same experience for £12 – the cost of the two-course lunch deal. But beware – wine prices kick off at £19 a bottle (£5.50 a glass). / www.blueelephant.com; midnight, Sun 10.30 pm; closed Sat L (except Stamford Bridge match days).

Blue Jade SW1   **£19**

44 Hugh St   7828 0321   2–4B

Year in year out, this unassuming Thai in a Pimlico backstreet plods steadily along delivering a good-value experience, most remarkable for the warmth of its service. The food's good too, though, and you could eat à la carte here at any time without busting the budget – chicken satay to start is £5.25 and a green curry main dish £7.95. If you're in the area for lunch, check out their 2-course deal for just £11.95, quaffing house wine at £13.95 a bottle. / 11 pm; closed Sat L & Sun.

Bocca Di Lupo W1   **£20***   A★★

12 Archer St   7734 2223   3–2D

Tucked away in a boring street near Piccadilly Circus, this shiny new Italian was one of the best arrivals of 2008. A duo of ex-Moro chefs deliver a wonderful menu of regional dishes, so it's worth the care needed to stick to our budget. Doing so is made easier by the menu format – all dishes come in small and large sizes – and by the offer of a menu of "One-Dish Meals" pre-7pm. Taking two small dishes from the à la carte, you might have chestnut & porcini soup (£6) followed by pork & foie gras sausage (£6.50). The wine list is excellent and keenly priced, with glasses from a mere £2.40, or a 500ml carafe for £8.70. / www.boccadilupo.com; midnight; closed Sun.

Boiled Egg & Soldiers SW11   **£16**

63 Northcote Rd   7223 4894   10–2C

On weekdays, this celebrated café at the heart of Wandsworth's 'Nappy Valley' is the official rendezvous for the local nannies and their charges. At weekends, however, it's known for the hangover-curative properties of its popular fry-ups – a full English will set you back £7.50. In addition to the café menu, there are a few more bistro-style items, such as a steak sandwich (£8.95). / L & afternoon tea only; no Mastercard or Amex; no booking.

Il Bordello E1 £25*

75-81 Wapping High St 7481 9950 11–1A

This ever-buzzing old-style Italian has long been a fixture of Wapping life. It's the sort of place you could easily overspend our budget, but it's perfectly easy to stay within it too if you opt for the pasta and (house-specialty) pizza dishes (from £7.95), washed down with house wine at £12.75 a bottle. / 11 pm; closed Sat L.

La Bouchée SW7 £20* 🄰

56 Old Brompton Rd 7589 1929 5–2B

This cramped and oh-so-French bistro, near South Kensington tube, is a notably busy and romantic destination by night. Sadly – thanks not least to house wine at £16.50 a bottle – it's not within our budget then, but this place also makes a cosy lunch venue, when a simple and very traditionally French meal – think soup and steak/frites – will set you back £11.50. / www.boudinblanc.co.uk; 11 pm.

Boulevard WC2 £20*

40 Wellington St 7240 2992 4–3D

It looks little different from the many tourist traps around Covent Garden, but this well-established bistro/brasserie has for many years now offered a dependable (if hardly earth-shattering) formula, and a civilised welcome. The best deal is at lunch and pre-theatre, when two courses are available for £11.95 (noon-7pm). You might have duck parfait, then minute steak (with meat from Donald Russell, the Queen's butcher, no less) with béarnaise sauce & fries. House wine is £13.95 a bottle. / www.boulevardbrasserie.co.uk; midnight.

Bradley's NW3 £21* ★

25 Winchester Rd 7722 3457 8–2A

A somewhat obscure location – in a Swiss Cottage sidestreet that's obviously convenient for nothing but the Hampstead Theatre – induces this smart local restaurant to offer bargains both at lunch and pre-theatre. At lunch you can have just a single course (£9.50). In the early-evening – or if your feeling hungry at lunch – it's two courses for £12.50. You might have pan fried ox tongue, beans & artichoke, followed by home salt beef, root vegetables & dumplings. House wine is £3.50 a glass. / www.bradleysnw3.co.uk; 11 pm; closed Sun D.

Brady's SW18 £18 ★

513 Old York Rd 8877 9599 10–2B

One of the relatively few places to do some sort of justice to our great national dish of fish 'n' chips, this Wandsworth bistro has a devoted local following. You could start with potted shrimps (£3.95), followed by a large order of fish 'n' chips (from £7.95), washed down with house wine at £11.95 a bottle. There's even plenty of budget left for some apple crumble (£3.95)! / 10.30 pm; closed Mon L & Sun; no Amex; no booking.

Brick Lane Beigel Bake E1 £ 3 ★★

159 Brick Ln 7729 0616 1–2D

Everyone should visit this grungy, 24/7 legend at least once – ideally in the wee hours when it's famously a fuel station for ravenous clubbers. Expect to queue, though, practically any time of day or night. These are the prices time forgot – a filled beigel with cream cheese is 80p, a cup of tea 40p or a coffee is 50p. Still hungry? Freshly-baked beigels to take home are 20p a pop. / open 24 hours; no credit cards; no booking.

Brilliant UB2 £19 ★

72-76 Western Rd 8574 1928 1–3A

This much-acclaimed curry-lovers Mecca is plonked down in the midst of Suburban Southall (about 10 minutes walk from the station), but the excellent Punjabi cooking and low prices justify the trek. Starters are typically £3, with a main dish – say Karahi lamb – costing around £9. House wine has been £9 a bottle for years now, or a Cobra will set you back £3.50. Bollywood movies blaring from the TVs jazz up what at quieter times can seem a cavernous space. / www.brilliantrestaurant.com; 11.30 pm, Fri & Sat midnight; closed Mon, Sat L & Sun L; booking: weekends only.

La Brocca NW6 £20 𝔸

273 West End Ln 7433 1989 1–1B

West Hampstead locals love this trusty Italian cellar below a wine bar. It's a very reliable option for pizza and pasta, served with more character than you'd find in a chain. You don't have to tread carefully to stay within budget, as main courses are typically about £9-£10, and house wine a bargain £10.95 a bottle. / www.labrocca.co.uk; Sun-Thu 10.30 pm, Fri & Sat 11 pm; booking: max 8.

Brompton Bar & Grill SW3 £20* 𝔸★

243 Brompton Rd 7589 8005 5–2C

This Knightsbridge newcomer lives up to its name, and – if you're looking for a 'plain vanilla' stand-by in this glitzy part of town, it's ideal. Given that it's quite a smart place, some of the prices – wines from £10 a bottle in particular – are surprisingly reasonable. Even so, you're likely to test our price limit if you dine à la carte. No such problems if you stick to the 2-course set lunch menu (£12), which might be the likes of generous fishcakes, followed by boeuf bourgignonne. / www.bromptonbarandgrill.com; 11 pm.

Brula TW1 £23* ★

43 Crown Rd 8892 0602 1–4A

Even on the lunch deal, this quirky but civilised St Margaret's bistro is at the top of our price-range, but it's still worth seeking out. It offers three good Gallic courses for your money – the £14 set lunch might comprise wild mushrooms & polenta chips, grilled sea bass, then bread & butter pudding with hazelnut ice cream to finish. The exclusively French wine list kicks off at £14.50 a bottle. / www.brula.co.uk; 10.30 pm.

Bull and Last NW5 £24 ★★

168 Highgate Rd 7267 3641 8–2B

A rave newspaper review helped put this unpretentious new Dartmouth Park gastropub quickly on the map, and it's all true – it really does offer remarkably good cooking. Prices are not bargain-basement – fish 'n' chips is £12, for example – but standards are as high as you will find anywhere. For a light meal, we'd suggest one of the generous starters, such as duck egg on toast (£7), and a pudding to share, such as clafoutis (£6.50), washed down with a glass of wine for around £4.

sign up for the survey at hardens.com 24

Buona Sera £20 A
289a King's Rd, SW3 7352 8827 5–3C
22 Northcote Rd, SW11 7228 9925 10–2C
There are two outlets of this jolly Italian chain. The family-friendly Battersea one is the more obviously 'budget' destination, but the Chelsea branch – which inherited weird 'double-decker' seating from a previous incarnation called 'The Jam' – also makes a fun destination in a pricey part of town. You need to take some care to stay within our price bracket, but – with a big range of pizzas and pastas, few of which exceed £8.50, and wines from £12.50 bottle – it's really not too hard. / midnight; SW3 closed Mon L.

Busaba Eathai £14 A
106-110 Wardour St, W1 7255 8686 3–2D
8-13 Bird St, W1 7518 8080 3–1A
22 Store St, WC1 7299 7900 2–1C
If you're looking for style on a tight budget, try this chain of low-lit noodle canteens. Pad Thai (£7.20) followed by green chicken curry (£7.50) might be a typical meal, washed down by house wine at £16 a bottle, or Thai beers at £3.50. A huge national expansion plan has been announced – they're going to have their work cut out to keep up the standards! / 11 pm, Fri & Sat 11.30 pm, Sun 10 pm; W1 no booking; WC1 need 12+ to book .

Butlers Wharf Chop House SE1 £19* A★
36e Shad Thames 7403 3403 9–4D
Magnificent views of Tower Bridge are the highlight at this modern English restaurant founded by Sir Terence Conran. As house wine at £17.50 a bottle hints, it's a pricey place (and, at à la carte prices, offers questionable value). An ace-value bar meal – always available – has, however, long been a feature. Your two courses for £10 might comprise carrot & orange soup, followed by grilled salmon. / www.chophouse.co.uk; 10.45 pm.

La Buvette TW9 £21 ★
6 Church Walk 8940 6264 1–4A
Much of the appeal of this classic French bistro (a sibling to St Margaret's Brula) is its quirky location – a tranquil churchyard that's somewhat at odds with its position in central Richmond. Just outside the budget for dinner with set menus starting at £17, its best value is the 2-course lunch – say potted smoked haddock, then daube of lamb – for £12.75. House wine is £13.75 a bottle. / www.labuvette.co.uk; 10.30 pm.

Byron £14 A
Ariel Way, W12 8743 7755 7–1C
222 Kensington High St, W8 7361 1717 5–1A
This mushrooming chain of posh burger restaurants is taking the capital by storm, combining quality burgers (a classic cheeseburger is £5.75, french fries are £2.75) with much smarter surroundings than its 'kitchen'-style competitors. For drinks, a shake will set you back £3.50, wine starts at £13.50 a bottle, and there's a good selection of beers (say Brooklyn Lager at £3.50 for a 330ml bottle). / www.byronhamburgers.com.

C&R Cafe W1 £18 ★
3-4 Rupert Ct 7434 1128 4–3A
This basic café in a Chinatown back alley has quite a following among Malalysian expats. If roti chanai (flatbread, £5) and mi goreng (fried noodles, £6.50) is your sort of thing, this may well be the place to enjoy it, especially as house wine is only £9.95 a bottle. / 11 pm.

Café 209 SW6 £14 A

209 Munster Rd 7385 3625 10–1B

For a decent budget dinner, with a good laugh thrown in, try this tiny BYO (corkage £1.90) Chinese/Thai café in deepest Fulham, presided over by extrovert and ever-present owner Joy. Best-sellers on the keenly-priced menu include the likes of chicken satay (£4.15) and green curry (£5.45). Beware, though – it's quite a crush, and some of the younger locals seem to have broken their volume controls. / 10.30 pm; D only, closed Sun, closed Dec; no Amex.

Café de Maya NW8 £14

4 Langtree Walk 7209 0672 8–3A

Moving to a new location near Swiss Cottage as this guide goes to press, this Oriental veteran serves up interesting Thai and Malay dishes at notably reasonable prices – Thai fishcakes (£3.80) and chicken with sweet basil (£5.25), for example. Puddings for £2.95 and a bottle of house wine for a mere £7.90 add to the place's charms. / 11 pm; D only, closed Mon; no Amex.

Café des Amis WC2 £22*

11-14 Hanover Pl 7379 3444 4–2D

Need a quick bite in Covent Garden? Ignore the ground and first floors of this restaurant – cutely situated in a alleyway, right by the Royal Opera House – and head instead for the basement bar. It can be a bit of a scrum, but there's a well-chosen (French) wine list starting at £16, and wonderful cheese and charcuterie platters for about a tenner (plus a selection of other inexpensive dishes). / www.cafedesamis.co.uk; 11.30 pm; closed Sun D.

Café du Jardin WC2 £21* A★

28 Wellington St 7836 8769 4–3D

In the minefield of Covent Garden rip-off joints, this bright corner restaurant is especially worth knowing about, and most particularly for the set menus available at lunch, and pre- and post-theatre which provide two courses and coffee for £13.50. You might have herb risotto, followed by fillet of salmon, and – for £3 more – a chocolate mousse. House wine is £12.50 a bottle. / www.lecafedujardin.com; Midnight, Sun 11 pm.

Café Emm W1 £15

17 Frith St 7437 0723 4–2A

This popular Soho bistro would probably not be first choice for a romantic assignation, but it's very popular with a young-at-heart crowd for its reasonably-priced meals. There's a 3-course set dinner menu, for example for £8.95 – you might find yourself having ham hock terrine, chargrilled salmon on pesto mash, and a chocolate pot. The house wine is £12.50 a bottle. / www.cafeemm.com; 10.30 pm, Fri-Sat 11.30 pm; no Amex; no booking after 6.30 pm.

Café in the Crypt
St Martin's in the Fields WC2 £15

Duncannon St 7766 1158 2–2C

There are no fireworks when it comes to the self-service café in the recently refurbished crypt of St Martin-in-the-Fields. This said, though, the setting makes this a more-than-usually atmospheric spot for a light bite in the heart of the West End, and at prices that don't raise too many eyebrows. Afternoon tea (from 2pm-6pm) includes a scone with jam & Cornish clotted cream, slice of Madiera cake and chocolate fudge cake with tea or coffee for £5.25. / www.stmartin-in-the-fields.org; Sun 6 pm, Mon-Tue 7.30 pm, Wed-Sat 10 pm; no Amex; no booking.

Café Japan NW11 £15 ★
626 Finchley Rd 8455 6854 1–1B
Near Golders Green Station, this cheerful and extremely authentic Japanese fixture has made quite a name for itself. Sushi (which starts from £2 a plate) is the main point – there are hot dishes, but they're rather incidental. Wash your meal down with house wine at £8.50 a bottle, a glass of hot sake (£2.80) or a Japanese beer (around £3). / www.cafejapan.co.uk; 10 pm; closed Mon, Tue, & Wed L-Fri L; no Amex.

Café Laville W2 £15 Ⓐ
453 Edgware Rd 7706 2620 8–4A
Looks aren't everything... but they sure help, which is why we've included this ultra-cute café, set on a bridge overlooking lovely Little Venice. No, the food's not anything special, but it's still a good perch for breakfast or a snack later in the day. A dish like bruschetta is £3.80 or a pasta and pesto £8.60. House wine is £14.50 a bottle. / 11 pm, Sun 10 pm; no Amex.

Café Mozart N6 £18 Ⓐ
17 Swains Ln 8348 1384 8–1B
If you're planning a walk on Hampstead Heath (or have just completed one), this pâtisserie/bistro is well worth knowing about. You can kick the day off with a good English breakfast (from £6.75) but as the day progresses, there's a Mitteleuropean flavour to most of the dishes, so the special might be schnitzel Holstein (£10.50), and there are also salads and fancy sandwiches (£4.50-£8). The house wine is £10 a bottle. / 10 pm; closed Mon D; no Amex; no booking at L.

Caffé Vergnano £18 Ⓐ★
62 Charing Cross Rd, WC2 7240 8587 4–3B
Royal Festival Hall, SE1 7921 9339 2–3D
Discerning caffeine addicts are often hooked on this small chain run by the eponymous coffee brand. While getting your fix, you can snack too – with antipasti from £4.90-£11.10, or there's a tempting array of puddings, like fruit panna cotta around £6. They also offer main courses such as fusilli with chicken & artichoke (£10.80), and even wines, from £14.95 a bottle. / www.caffevergnano1882.co.uk.

La Cage Imaginaire NW3 £21* Ⓐ
16 Flask Walk 7794 6674 8–1A
Almost a parody of a sweet little restaurant, this long-established Gallic joint, prettily tucked-away just off Hampstead's main drag, is pretty reasonably-priced at any time of day. It's only truly a budget destination for lunch, though, when a 2-course set menu – perhaps calamari, avocado & cherry tomato salad followed by oven roasted lamb roulade – will set you back just £10.95. A glass of house wine is £4.75. / 11 pm.

Camino N1 £19*
3 Varnishers Yd, Regent Quarter 7841 7331 8–3C
Down a King's Cross alleyway, this laid back Spanish joint is a bright spark in what's still a fairly dull area. In the evening you'd spend over our budget here, but during the week there's a 2-course menu for £12, and a 3-course one for £15: perhaps a bean & sausage casserole then braised lamb shanks (and – if you're still going – almond tart to finish). House wine is £12.75 a bottle. / www.barcamino.com; 11 pm.

Carnevale EC1 £20* ★

135 Whitecross St   7250 3452   9–1B

This chic veggie deli, near the Barbican, serves very good sandwiches (from £2.25), as well as a full menu of enterprising dishes. A la carte, you could rather stretch our budget, but there's a 3-course (or 2-course plus glass of wine) menu available until 7pm (£13.50), from which your choice might be asparagus salad with mizuna, followed by baked plum tomato risotto with wild garlic leaves & Parmesan, finishing up with chocolate & chestnut roulade. House wine is £7.50 for half a litre. / www.carnevalerestaurant.co.uk; 11 pm; closed Sat L & Sun; no Amex.

Casa Brindisa SW7 £22 ★

7-9 Exhibition Rd   7590 0008   5–2C

Handily located right by South Kensington tube, this latest tapas bar offshoot of the famous Spanish food importer, Brindisa, offers very good standard tapas at reasonable, if not super-bargain prices. More basic dishes are around the £4 mark, about the same cost as the standard wines by the glass. For children visiting the local museums, a three-course set lunch menu (£8.50) is available at the weekends. / www.casabrindisa.com.

Cây Tre EC1 £20 ★

301 Old St   7729 8662   9–1B

It may be just round the corner from Hoxton Square, but this low-key Vietnamese is the very antithesis of trendiness. This has done nothing to prevent it building up quite a following, thanks to offering good and spicy food at very reasonable prices – most of the meat dishes, for example, are somewhere round the £8 mark, and wine prices kick off at £11 a bottle. / www.vietnamesekitchen.co.uk; 11 pm, Fri-Sat 11.30 pm, Sun 10.30 pm.

Centrepoint Sushi WC2 £18 Ⓐ★

20-21 St Giles High St   7240 6147   4–1B

Above a Korean supermarket in the shadow of Centre Point, this friendly little Japanese café seems a slightly unlikely find. It's worth remembering, though, when you next need a quality bite in the centre of town, with bento boxes ranging from £8.50, and house wine costing a modest £10 a bottle. / www.cpfs.co.uk; 10.30 pm; closed Sun.

Le Cercle SW1 £24 Ⓐ★

1 Wilbraham Pl   7901 9999   5–2D

This elegant establishment near Sloane Square is by no means a budget destination in the normal sense. However, the £15, 3-course lunch menu (including tea or coffee) offers a great opportunity to check it out (and, being a basement, it feels the same night and day). The French tapas-style dishes are some of the most accomplished food of their type in town, and the wine list – focussed on the south west of France – is of very high quality. Unfortunately, it kicks off at £20 a bottle. / www.lecercle.co.uk; 11 pm; closed Mon & Sun.

Cha Cha Moon £16 Ⓐ

15-21 Ganton St, W1   7297 9800   3–2C
151 Queensway, W2   5–1C

A generous one-price-fits-all policy (all dishes £3.50) helped über-restaurateur Alan Yau's Soho newcomer make a big splash when it launched in mid-2008. Nowadays, some of the (generally quite small) Oriental dishes are a couple of pounds more, so it's not quite such a bargain, especially as a glass of wine – albeit a 250ml one – weighs in at £4.95. Trend-seekers, however, will probably still feel that at least one visit is worthwhile.

Chakalaka SW15 £21* ★

136 Upper Richmond Rd 8789 5696 10–2B

*A South African theme helps create a fun vibe at this plain but
sociable spot near East Putney tube. If you opt for the springbok loin
you'll bust the budget, but they do a £14 weekday dinner or weekend
lunch deal which includes four tapas-style dishes (such as vegetables
samosas, chicken wings, or boerewors sausage). House wine is £14
a bottle. (The new Chiswick branch offers a weekday deal to delight
any carnivore – all the ribs you can eat for £13.95!)
/ www.chakalakarestaurant.com; 10.45 pm.*

Chamomile NW3 £19

45 England's Ln 7586 4580 8–2B

*Tucked away in Belsize Park, this chilled spot is the kind of place
everyone wishes they had on the doorstep for whiling away time over
the papers and brunch. Originally it just did cakes and a bit
of breakfast, but the menu has expanded over the years and now all
day (but not in the evening) they serve the likes of vegetable lasagne
(£7) and shepherd's pie (£8). Wine starts at £11 a bottle. / 6 pm;
L only; no Amex.*

Charles Lamb N1 £23 Ⓐ

16 Elia St 7837 5040 8–3D

*This somewhat Frenchified gastropub yearling is a useful find in the
backstreets behind Angel tube, with pricing that's a shade more
reasonable than many of its rivals. Starters and puddings are
generally about a fiver (from potted crab, to pecan pie) with
most mains around a tenner (like merguez sausages with Puy lentils).
There's a good selection of draught beers and lagers, and wine from
£13 a bottle. / www.thecharleslambpub.com; 9.30 pm; closed Mon L,
Tue L & Sun D; no Amex; no booking.*

Chelsea Bun Diner SW10 £16

9a Lamont Rd 7352 3635 5–3B

*Breakfasts at this Chelsea café are sometimes claimed to be the
ultimate hangover cure. Arrive during the week by midday,
and options start from £3.80. At any time you can have a 'gourmet'
option – for example a 'Malibu Omelette' (a 4-egg omelette with
salmon, avocado & Mascarpone, plus hash browns, plus tea
or coffee, £8.95). There's also a large all-day diner menu. House wine
is £9.90 a bottle. / www.chelseabun.co.uk; midnight, Sun 10 pm; no Amex;
no booking, Sat & Sun.*

Chez Liline N4 £23* ★★

101 Stroud Green Rd 7263 6550 8–1D

*From outside, this Mauritian fish restaurant in Finsbury Park looks
a bit grungy. Once you're inside it's not that much nicer! Don't
be discouraged, though – you can try some of the best, spicy fish
in town here. To stay within budget, you'll have to stick to the 2-
course set menu for £15 available at lunch and dinner (Sunday-
Thursday). You might have prawns with ginger & spring onion then
red snapper in Creole sauce. House wine is £11.75 a bottle. / 11 pm;
closed Sun L.*

Chez Lindsay TW10 £18* A★
11 Hill Rise   8948 7473   1–4A

This pleasant café is a stone's throw from Richmond Bridge. It's an attractive, easy-going sort of place, and offers a slightly 'different' Breton menu, majoring in crêpes, seafood and ciders. Mostly it's out of our price range, but there is a good-value 2-course lunch menu for £9.75. This is hearty fare – say grilled mushrooms with ham & ratatouille, topped with melting cheese, then mixed fish & seafood gratin. Wine is £14.95 a bottle, or a large bottle of cider starts at £9.50. / www.chezlindsay.co.uk; 11 pm; no Amex.

Chez Marcelle W14 £18 ★★
34 Blythe Rd   7603 3241   7–1D

Patronne Marcelle is the driving force at this very personal spot, behind Olympia. She's not so hot on interior design, but how she makes money at such reasonable prices mystifies some fans of the lovingly-prepared Lebanese dishes. Starters (such as moussaka) are around £4, mains (say stuffed clams) are £9.50. House wine is just £10.50 a bottle, or drink mint tea at £1.50 a cup. / 10 pm; closed Mon, Tue-Thu D only, Fri-Sun open L & D; no credit cards.

Chez Patrick W8 £20* ★
7 Stratford Rd   7937 6388   5–2A

Being hidden away in a charming Kensington backwater is a mixed blessing for this traditional Gallic fish restaurant, but it's good news for customers, as it offers an eye-catching, 3-course lunch to pull in the business. For £12.50 (£15.50 at weekends) you might have oysters to start, scallop ravioli to follow, with chocolate moelleux to finish. The exclusively French wine list starts at £11 a bottle. / www.chezpatrickinlondon.co.uk; 11 pm; closed Sun D.

Chi Noodle & Wine Bar EC4 £18 A
5 New Bridge St   7353 2409   9–2A

This family-run City Oriental is a welcome alternative to the Wagamamas of the world, and a good spot for after-work as well as lunchtime refuelling. A selection like grilled beef ramen is £7.90, and a non-noodle dish like salt & chilli squid comes in at £5.90. Wine is available (£11.95 for the house), or drink Tsingtao beer at £3 a bottle. / www.chinoodle.com; 10.30 pm; closed Sat & Sun.

China Boulevard on the River SW18 £18* ★
1 The Boulevard, Smugglers Way   8871 3881   10–2B

The location – in a modern development near Wandsworth Bridge – is out-on-a-limb, but that doesn't stop this large Thames-side Oriental, with sweeping views, from being regularly packed with Oriental diners. You'd have to scrimp to dine here within our price range, but it's no problem at lunch, when there's a wide-ranging dim sum menu, with most dishes around £2-£3 (and half-price on weekdays). Better go easy on the vino, though – it's £14 a bottle. / www.chinaboulevard.com; 11 pm; no Maestro.

The Chinese Experience W1 £19
118-120 Shaftesbury Ave   7437 0377   4–3A

One of the friendlier Chinatown destinations, this bright contemporary spot is a good all-rounder, ideally situated for a pre- or post-theatre dinner. With most standard main courses somewhere around the £8 mark, it's not hard to eat here within budget at any time. Even better, dim sum are served here for both lunch and dinner – most dishes are around the £3 mark. House wine is £14 a bottle. / www.chineseexperience.com; 11 pm.

Chisou W1   £24   ★
4 Princes St 7629 3931 3–1C
This quietly quirky Japanese café, just off Hanover Square – run by
an Englishman (who has won awards in Japan for his knowledge
of sake) and his Japanese wife – gives little hint that it is one of the
West End's better Orientals. With care you could dine here within our
budget, but at lunchtime, when set meals start at £9, it's a cinch.
House sake is £4.10 a glass. / www.chisou.co.uk; 10.30 pm; closed Sun.

Chop'd   £12   ★
52 Curzon St, W1   7495 1014   3–3B
St Pancras International, NW1   7837 1603   8–3C
Unit 1 34 The North Colonnade, E14   3229 0087   11–1C
2 Horner Sq, Old Spitalfields Mkt, E1   7247 8757   9–1D
2 Leadenhall Mkt, EC3   7626 3706   9–2D
One of the better value, designer-salad brands springing up around
the capital, with most of its 'ready to go' selection costing about
a fiver; 'create your own' is £6.50. There's also a similarly priced
range of 'hot pot' alternatives (say spicy meatball pasta for £4.75).
Branches are unlicensed: a juice or cordial will set you back £1-£2.
/ www.chopd.co.uk; L only.

Chowki W1   £21   ★
2-3 Denman St   7439 1330   3–2D
It's not quite the top-value destination it once was, but the sheer
convenience of the location of this contemporary-style establishment –
hard by Piccadilly Circus – makes this Indian restaurant worth
knowing about. You need to choose reasonably carefully to stay within
our price bracket, but with many main courses around the £10 mark,
it's perfectly possible. Wines kick off at £12.95 a bottle.
/ www.chowki.com; 11.30 pm.

Chuen Cheng Ku W1   £17
17 Wardour St   7437 1398   4–3A
This frenetic landmark offers a classic Chinatown experience,
particularly its well-known dim sum, when trollies laden with
mysterious bites criss-cross crazily round the vast dining rooms. You
may not like everything you choose, but with prices starting at £1.95,
mistakes are not particularly costly. Evening prices might stretch our
budget, unless you go for the (hackneyed) set meals, starting
at £9.80. House wine is £13.20 a bottle. / www.chuenchengku.co.uk;
11.45 pm.

Churchill Arms W8   £15   𝔸★
119 Kensington Church St   7792 1246   6–2B
This crowded Notting Hill boozer is the finest example in the capital
of that singularly British phenomenon: the Thai-in-a-pub. You eat in a
cosily chaotic annex (aka The Butterfly Room), where about
20 excellent dishes are offered at a mind-bogglingly cheap £6-£7.
Complete the experience with the determinedly un-Thai puds: apple
pie, for instance, will set you back £2.50. House wine is £11.95
a bottle, or a pint of Stella is £3.55. / 10 pm; closed Sun D.

Chutney SW18   £16   ★
11 Alma Rd   8870 4588   10–2B
There's nothing particularly 'different' about this excellent Indian
restaurant in Wandsworth, it just does what it does very well,
and with a smile. A typical curry such as chicken jalfrezi will set you
back £6.95, and you don't have to try too hard to eat within our
budget at any time. Drink a small bottle of Cobra for £2.50.
/ 11.30 pm; D only.

Chutneys NW1 £14 ★

124 Drummond St 7388 0604 8–4C

Long a linchpin of the 'Little India' behind Euston station, this simple veggie café is best known for its lunchtime buffet (£6.95, also served all day on Sunday). At other times, dishes such as pooris (deep-fried, stuffed chapatis) cost only £3.60, and even the most expensive main courses are only around £7. A bottle of the house wine is £9.95. / 11 pm; no Amex; need 5+ to book.

Ciao Bella WC1 £22 A★

86-90 Lamb's Conduit St 7242 4119 2–1D

Perhaps the most popular reasonably-priced central trattoria, this long-established, tightly-packed and noisy bastion of Bloomsbury life is popular for a good reason – it offers solid standards at very reasonable prices. The true budget option is to go for a main-course pasta or pizza (around £7), but – with house wine kicking off at £12 a bottle – you might decide you can afford to be a bit more adventurous. Relatively speaking, of course. / www.ciaobellarestaurant.co.uk; 11.30 pm, Sun 10.30 pm.

Clifton E1 £18 ★

1 Whitechapel Rd 7377 5533 9–2D

Brick Lane's curry houses may be known internationally, but the truth is that none of its restaurants have individually achieved any great fame. This well-established spot – part of a group with also includes the nearby Shampan (which isn't bad either) – is certainly better in all ways than most options hereabouts, and it falls happily within our budget at all times (especially if you go for their 2-course deal for £12). House wine is £9.95 a bottle. / www.cliftonrestaurant.com; midnight, Sat & Sun 1am.

Clos Maggiore WC2 £25* A★

33 King St 7379 9696 4–3C

Even if you stick to the 2-course lunch and pre-theatre deal for £19.50 (including a glass of wine), you will – technically speaking – break our budget on a visit to this notably attractive Franco/Italian restaurant in the heart of Covent Garden. We think it's worth bringing it to your attention, though, as its high standards notably resist the temptations of its tourist-trap location, and the hidden-away covered 'courtyard' really is one of the most romantic locations in London. / www.closmaggiore.com; 10.45 pm, Sat 11.15 pm, Sun 10 pm; closed Sat L & Sun L.

Club Mangia
The Punch Tavern EC4 £16 A

99 Fleet St 7353 6658 9–2A

This quirky City tavern is long on historical and literary interest, but avoids the 'dry' feeling of many ancient City haunts, feeling rather more like a coffee-house. An unusual lunchtime food 'offer' – a help-yourself buffet for £7.95 – adds further character (and there's also a pricier à la carte). You can have a pint of ale (£3.20), or drink house wine at £13 a bottle. / www.punchtavern.com; 11.30 pm, Thu & Fri midnight; closed Sat D & Sun.

Cochonnet W9 £18 ★

1 Lauderdale Pde 7289 0393 1–2B

A busy local in Maida Vale with dependable pizza and pasta dishes (around £10), as well as a superior and well-priced wine list (from £12.50 a bottle). / www.cochonnet.co.uk; 10.30pm, pizza until close at midnight.

Cock Tavern EC1 £23

Smithfield Mkt   7248 2918   9–2A

*For the committed carnivore, there's something about coming
to Smithfield Market (the heart of London's meat trade) for an early
morning fry-up (in particular at one of the pubs licensed to serve beer
from dawn). This cellar tavern is no great shakes atmosphere-wise, but
offers a definitive full English for £4.25, which you can wash down
with a pint of Fosters for £2.90. The food's not bad at lunch either
(when roast beef and Yorkshire will set you back £12.95). / 5 pm;
closed Sat & Sun.*

Le Colombier SW3 £23* A★

145 Dovehouse St   7351 1155   5–2C

*Hidden away on a Chelsea corner – and with one of the
nicest terraces of any restaurant in town – this archetypal Gallic
brasserie offers just the menu you'd expect. It's way beyond our price
limit à la carte – check out your fellow diners, and you'll see why –
but makes a splendid sunny-day lunching destination, when two
courses will set you back £16.50. There's a high quality, all-French
wine list from £13.50 a bottle. / www.lecolombier-sw3.co.uk; 10.30 pm,
Sun 10 pm.*

Cork & Bottle WC2 £23 A

44-46 Cranbourn St   7734 7807   4–3B

*Don Hewitson's much-loved West End wine bar is now heading for
40 years under his ownership. It has two principal attractions –
an implausible basement location, next to a Leicester Square sex
shop, and a lovingly maintained wine list (from £15.95 a bottle). The
food is rather incidental – two courses at lunch will set you back
£11.50, or a substantial à la carte main course – such as shepherd's
pie with chips (sic) and salad – is about the same.
/ www.corkandbottle.net; 11.30 pm; no booking after 6.30 pm.*

Costa's Fish Restaurant W8 £14 ★

18 Hillgate St   7727 4310   6–2B

*This Greek chippy (by the taverna of the same name) is an
unchanging feature of Hillgate Village (as local estate agents describe
these cute streets off Notting Hill Gate). It's a cosy, old-fashioned spot
for cod 'n' chips at £8.40 a portion. House vino is £11.50 a bottle,
or drink Keo lager for £3.40 a time. / 10 pm; closed Mon & Sun; no credit
cards.*

Costa's Grill W8 £15

12-14 Hillgate St   7229 3794   6–2B

*The Costa family opened this stalwart taverna in 1957, and it hasn't
changed much since. It's a refreshing antidote to some of its trendier
neighbours in nearby Notting Hill Gate. The scoff is very basic,
but comes at very cheap prices: a dish of taramasalata is £2.90,
Greek salad is £3.50, kleftiko is £8.90. You can complete the
experience with a bottle of retsina at £12 (house wine is £1 cheaper).
/ www.costasgrill.com; 10.30 pm; closed Sun (closed 3 weeks in Aug).*

The Cow W2 £21* A★

89 Westbourne Park Rd   7221 0021   6–1B

*As it gets older, Tom Conran's perennially trendy haunt for dressed-
down Notting Hillbillies looks ever more genuinely like the traditional
Irish boozer it was modelled on. Reflecting its market, this can
be quite a pricy destination – house wine, for example, is £15.75
a bottle, and a pint of Guinness is £3.60. The 'Cow Special' – six rock
oysters and a pint of Guinness for £11 – is the top deal, or you could
have the soup of the day (£5) followed by sausage 'n' mash (£9.50).
/ www.thecowlondon.co.uk; 10.30 pm; D only, Sun open L & D; no Amex.*

Crazy Homies W2 £19 A★

127 Westbourne Park Rd 7727 6771 6–1B

Part of the Conran empire (Tom Conran that is, son of Sir Terence), this funky Mexican cantina on the Notting Hill/Bayswater borders offers the chance to hang out with the local cool crowd, while being kind on your wallet. Quality is high, and tacos, burros and enchiladas – mainly under a tenner – are dependably well made. Don't blow all your savings by getting trashed! A classic margarita will set you back £7.50, and bottled beers are £3.50 and up.

/ www.crazyhomieslondon.co.uk; 10.30 pm; closed weekday L; no Amex.

Crussh £10

1 Curzon St, W1 7629 2554 3–3B
BBC Media Village, Wood Ln, W12 8746 7916 6–2A
27 Kensington High St, W8 7376 9786 5–1A
One Canada Sq, E14 7513 0076 11–1C
Unit 21 Jubilee Pl, E14 7519 6427 11–1C
48 Cornhill, EC3 7626 2175 9–2C
6 Farringdon St, EC4 7489 5916 9–2A

For a healthy bite that's full of flavour, this simple chain hits the spot. Smoothies and juices are the house speciality – from £3 for a 'medium' size one – and there's also a well-made range of salads, soups and sarnies for a similar price. / www.crussh.com; 4.30 pm - 7 pm; some branches closed all or part of weekend; no credit cards.

Cumberland Arms W14 £24

29 North End Rd 7371 6806 7–2D

Like many gastropubs, this Olympia destination is not in fact that cheap. It is, though, just about the only bright spark at the top of the North End Road, and if you stick to the less expensive dishes, you can eat well here – perhaps a plate of pasta (£10), followed by chocolate cake and cream £5 – and stay within our budget. Wine prices, kicking off at £12.50 a bottle, are pretty reasonable too, and there's a decent range for those prepared to spend a few pounds more. / www.thecumberlandarmspub.co.uk; 10.30 pm, Sun 10 pm.

Cyprus Mangal SW1 £18 ★

45 Warwick Way 7828 5940 2–4B

The heart of Pimlico isn't a top dining destination, nor is this no-frills pit stop strong on interior design. On the plus side, though, it's a friendly place with superior kebabs and good prices: starters are £3.50-£5.50, mains £8-£11, and house wine £10 a bottle. / Sun-Thu midnight, Fri & Sat 1 am; no Amex.

The Czechoslovak Restaurant NW6 £18

74 West End Ln 7372 1193 1–1B

The dated styling of this long-running émigrés club in West Hampstead has scarcely been improved by a recent make-over, and much of the charm is still of a retro nature. The hearty traditional fodder certainly makes a change, though, and ain't expensive: a starter like vyvar s nudlemi (broth with noodles) is £3; a typical main dish like segedinsky gulás and knedlíky (pork goulash with dumplings and sauerkraut) is £7.50. A pint of draught Budvar will set you back £3.30. / www.czechoslovak-restaurant.co.uk; 10 pm; closed Mon, Tue-Fri D only, Sat & Sun open L & D; no credit cards.

Da Mario SW7 £21

15 Gloucester Rd   7584 9078   5–1B

Of particular note if you're looking for somewhere to eat around the Royal Albert Hall, this grandly-housed but cosy Italian of long standing offers all the standard pizzas and pastas, generally priced at £8-10, with house wines from about £13 a bottle. (Downstairs, there's a slightly improbable dine 'n' disco cellar suited to parties, but priced a bit above a true 'budget' level.) / www.damario.co.uk; 11.30 pm.

Dalchini SW19 £22   A★

147 Arthur Rd   8947 5966   10–2B

This Wimbledon Park fixture is a good all-rounder, and also one of those places you can have a bit of a culinary adventure, and keep within our budget. The cooking is "Hakka Chinese", which might crudely be described as Indian with a bit of Chinese thrown in. Whatever you call it, it's very satisfying. And even à la carte you can dine here within our budget, although top deals are to be had at lunch (from £5.95) and early evening (till 7pm, from £7.95). House wine is £11.90 a bottle. / www.dalchini.co.uk; 10.30 pm, Fri & Sat 11 pm; no Amex.

Daphne NW1 £15*

83 Bayham St   7267 7322   8–3C

This cosy Greek taverna in Camden Town – not to be confused with the swanky Daphne's at Brompton Cross – has long been a haven of good value and filling nosh. You could have their 3-course mezze dinner (£16.50) and still squeeze within budget here, but the keenest deal is at lunch (2-course for £7.75, 3-course for £9.25). Wine starts at £3.25 a glass. / 11.30 pm; closed Sun; no Amex.

Daquise SW7 £18

20 Thurloe St   7589 6117   5–2C

By South Kensington tube, this cosy old time warp is one of London's great survivors, and has been doling out hearty Polish fodder – plus tea and cakes – since 1947. The food here isn't art, but it is cheap – for the 2-course set lunch (£9), you might have soup, with potato pancakes to follow. A la carte, you might have borscht (£3.30) followed by golabki (cabbage rolls, £8.50). House wine is £14 a bottle, or drink Zywiec Polish beer at £3.70. / 11 pm; no Amex.

De Cecco SW6 £21*

189 New King's Rd   7736 1145   10–1B

This classic neighbourhood Italian, near Parson's Green, isn't quite the hot destination it once was, but still does what it does very well. A la carte you'd push our price limit, but visit at lunch or early evening (6.30pm-8pm) and you can have a 2-course meal – perhaps salad followed by salmon pasta – for £12.95. House wine starts at £3.50 a glass. / www.dececcorestaurant.com; 11 pm; closed Sun D.

Dehesa W1 £20   A★★

25 Ganton St   7494 4170   3–2C

A spin off from the ever-popular Salt Yard, this fabulous new tapas bar has a great location, just off Carnaby Street, and already feels like an institution that will run and run. A tempting array of tapas are priced from £3.50-£7, and there's a wide range of similarly priced charcuterie, cheese and bar snacks, ensuring a reasonable choice for those counting the pennies. All this, plus a very tempting list of drinks, with wines ranging from £15-£300! / www.dehesa.co.uk; 11 pm; closed Sun D; no booking.

Del'Aziz £21* 𝔸

24-32 Vanston Pl, SW6   7386 0086   5–4A
Ariel Way, W12   8740 0666   7–1C
Adelaide Rd, NW3   7586 3338   8–2A
5 Canvey St, SE1   7633 0033   9–4B

Ever since it opened, the 'Aziz' restaurant in Fulham was outshone
by its neighbouring café/deli namesake, and the chain now spreading
across the capital is moulded on the latter. Though the menu is styled
as 'Mediterranean', it includes many Middle Eastern and Persian
dishes, plus burgers and breakfasts – many dishes costing around
a fiver. There's a 2-course set lunch (£12.50), which might comprise
the likes of a platter of seafood boreck, followed by grilled merguez
sausages with couscous, washed down with house wine at £12.50
a bottle. / www.delaziz.co.uk.

Delfino W1 £22

121 Mount St   7499 1256   3–3B

The area around Mayfair's Connaught hotel is hardly awash with
bargain eateries. All the more, then, worth knowing about this
friendly and cramped pizzeria, opposite. Its prices – pizzas (around
£10) and house wine for £12.90 a bottle – may not quite be bargain-
basement but, round here, they're as good as it gets. / www.finos.co.uk;
11 pm; closed Sat L & Sun.

La Delizia Limbara SW3 £16 ★

63-65 Chelsea Manor St   7376 4111   5–3C

The only remaining remnant of what was a small Chelsea chain
of pizzerias can still induce the occasional pang of nostalgia
amongst old regulars, who remember the days when its crisp styling
seemed to be very cutting-edge. The place still does good pizzas
(around £7) and other dishes such as asparagus risotto (£7.95),
and it's very reasonably priced by local standards. A bottle of the
house wine will set you back £12. / 11 pm; no Amex.

The Deptford Project SE8 £ 8

121-123 Deptford High St   1–3D

The location – a converted BR passenger carriage dumped by the
high street and transformed into a hippy-chic 57-seater café – is the
draw to this magnificently bonkers Deptford venture (especially
in summer, when the large terrace comes into its own). The scoff
is simple and inexpensive, including breakfast options such as a full
English (weekends only, £5.30). Sandwiches and buns are all under
a fiver. Fresh smoothies are £2.75. / www.thedeptfordproject.com.

Le Deuxième WC2 £21* ★

65a Long Acre   7379 0033   4–2D

This stark French restaurant could not be more convenient for the
Royal Opera House, and is always packed pre-performance. A la
carte, it's beyond our price range, but the lunchtime and pre-/post-
theatre deal are well within reach. For £13.50 you get two courses
(£16.50 for three), plus tea or coffee. These might be Caesar salad,
followed by grilled breast of chicken (and then, if you've gone the
whole hog, chocolate mousse), washed down with house wine
at £13.50 a bottle. / www.ledeuxieme.com; midnight, Sun 11 pm.

Dinings W1 £18* ★★
22 Harcourt St 7723 0666 8–4A
You'd better book ahead if you want to check out this bizarre bunker-style Japanese in Marylebone. The attraction? An ex-Nobu chef who has brought all his skills with him, and offers delicious dishes at a fraction of the cost. Unsurprisingly, you'd have to scrimp a bit to dine here within our price range, but at lunchtime – with set lunch menus ranging from £9.50-£16.50 – it's relatively easy. Wines start at £16 a bottle. / 10.30 pm; closed Sat L & Sun.

Diwana Bhel-Poori House NW1 £15 ★
121-123 Drummond St 7387 5556 8–4C
It must have looked pretty cutting edge in the '70s, but this stalwart veggie canteen in Euston's Little India is showing its age nowadays. But if standards aren't quite up to yesteryear, the grub is still tasty enough and prices are still laughably cheap (aided by the unusual boon, near central London, of being able to BYO). The top tips à la carte remain the pooris (£3.60) or thalis (£8.60), but the steal is still the lunchtime buffet (£6.95). / 10.45 pm; need 10+ to book.

don Fernando's TW9 £20 𝔸
27f The Quadrant 8948 6447 1–4A
Just by Richmond station, this large and lively, family-run tapas joint is equally suited to a quick convenient bite or a night out with friends. The usual tapas are available, many for £5-£6 each, but you could also have a main dish like lamb with rosemary (£9.95) and stay within budget. If it's party night, grab a jug of sangria for £13.25. / www.donfernando.co.uk; 11 pm; no Amex; no booking.

Don Pepe NW8 £20 𝔸
99 Frampton St 7262 3834 8–4A
London's oldest tapas bar is a very cheerful and authentic place, and makes an unlikely find in the no man's land, near Lord's. It's also notably reasonably priced, with all dishes between £2.50 and £6.50 and the cheapest item on the all-Hispanic wine list at just £10. (There's also a slightly posher restaurant off the bar, which falls just outside our price limit.) / 11.30 pm; closed Sun.

Dragon Castle SE17 £21
114 Walworth Rd 7277 3388 1–3C
The scale of this Chinese restaurant would be striking anywhere, but in Elephant & Castle it's nothing short of remarkable. The food can be pretty good too – for top value, seek out lunchtime dim sum (mainly £1.90), but, with care, you can eat here within our budget at any time. Set menus, for example, kick off at £14.80 a head, and wines (from quite a good selection) range from £12.80 a bottle. / www.dragoncastle.eu; 11 pm, Fri 11.30 pm, Sun 10.30 pm.

The Drunken Monkey E1 £21 𝔸
222 Shoreditch High St 7392 9606 9–1D
A funky Shoreditch bar with regular DJs playing 'music with soul for easy digestion'. There's a bar menu of dim sum (around £3-£4) or bigger noodle dishes (around £6) to help soak up an extensive list of cocktails, wines and beers, be it on draught (£3.90 for a pint of Hoegaarden) or bottled. If choice is too stressful, they do a set deal of £15 per person providing about 10 different dishes. / www.thedrunkenmonkey.co.uk; 11.45 pm; closed Sat L

The Duke's Head SW15   £20*   🅐

8 Lower Richmond Rd   8788 2552   10–1B

This grand riverside Putney tavern is – like many Young's pubs – a cut above the norm. Upstairs, the River View restaurant only falls easily within our budget for the set lunch menu, when two courses – perhaps langoustine & roast pear salad, followed by seared lamb chops & Savoy cabbage – will set you back £13.50. On the bar menu, though, you can always enjoy (slightly simpler) main courses, mostly for less than a tenner. A pint of bitter is £3.85. / www.dukesheadputney.co.uk; 10.30 pm.

Durbar W2   £19

24 Hereford Rd   7727 1947   6–1B

This endearing, old-fashioned Bayswater curry house has been around for 50 years, so presumably they are doing something right. Prices are those of a neighbourhood curry house, with the best deal being the meat thali set menu for £14.95 (for which you'd get chicken tikka, a kebab, lamb dupiaza, a bhajee, rice, and naan). House wine is £10.95 a bottle. / www.durbartandoori.co.uk; 11.30 pm; closed Fri.

The Eagle EC1   £22   ★

159 Farringdon Rd   7837 1353   9–1A

This cramped and always-buzzing Farringdon boozer is generally credited as the cradle, back in 1991, of the gastropub revolution which has now swept much of Britain (and even rippled out across the USA). Like many gastropubs, it's not actually that inexpensive, but you can just about squeeze a meal in here and stay within our budget – you might have mushroom bruschetta (£4.50), for example, followed by a Mediterranean fillet of pork (£12), washed down with house wine at £11.95 a bottle. / 10.30 pm; closed Sun D; no Amex; no booking.

Eagle Bar Diner W1   £16   🅐

3-5 Rathbone Pl   7637 1418   4–1A

Burgers (from about £7), hot dogs (from £4), shakes, and cocktails have made a winning formula for this cool spot. By day, it's a retreat from Oxford Street shopping, but by night it gets clubbier and louder. Drink beer (from about £3.50) or non-alcoholic shakes to stay within budget. Then again, those cocktails and 'hard shakes' (£7-£9) do look good... / www.eaglebardiner.com; Mon-Wed 11 pm, Thu-Sat 1 am; closed Sun D; no Amex; need 6+ to book.

Eco   £18   ★

144 Chiswick High Rd, W4   8747 4822   7–2A
162 Clapham High St, SW4   7978 1108   10–2D

A pair of pizzerias offering high-quality grub at reasonable prices – pizza (and pasta) dishes for less than a tenner (and wines from £12.50 a bottle). The '90s Clapham original is quite a local veteran, and remains very busy (and noisy). It's still early days for the Chiswick spin-off, whose hard-edged style seems slightly at odds with this more sedate neighbourhood. / www.ecorestaurants.com; SW4 11 pm.

Ed's Easy Diner £16 A

12 Moor St, W1 7434 4439 4–2A
19 Rupert St, W1 7287 1951 3–3D
15 Gt Newport St, WC2 7836 0271 4–3B

It's like stepping onto the set of 'Happy Days' at these retro '50s diners, whose appeal remains remarkably fresh, even though many of the branches have been around for over 20 years. The original hamburger is £5.05, and something fancy (like Ed's Chicken Caesar) is more like £7.95. Hungry? Mississippi mud pie fills a corner at £3.95. Go for a shake (£3.15) or a small bottle of Californian red wine at £3.95. / www.edseasydiner.co.uk; Rupert St 10 pm, Fri & Sat midnight; Moor St 11.30 pm, Fri & Sat midnight; no Amex; no booking at weekends.

Edokko WC1 £23 A★★

50 Red Lion St 7242 3490 2–1D

Barristers from nearby Gray's Inn often say nice things about this rickety-looking Japanese restaurant. The downstairs is diner-style, so for more atmosphere seek out the first floor (where you sit cross-legged at low tables). At dinner it's out of our price range, but at lunch they do various set menus starting from £10, and, for £16, you can have a set with some of their excellent sushi. Drink Sapporo beer at £3.30 a bottle, or unlimited green tea (50p). / 10 pm; closed Sat L & Sun; no Amex.

Eight Over Eight SW3 £19* A★

392 King's Rd 7349 9934 5–3B

This chic Chelsea hang-out is one of Will Ricker's stable of cool-crowd venues, which specialises in quality cocktails and Oriental tapas. Not a natural for this guide then, except at lunchtime when a good 3-course deal is offered for £15 – you might have miso soup, chicken or salmon salad and green tea ice cream. And it includes a glass of wine (normally £4 a glass, £16 a bottle). / www.rickerrestaurants.com; 11 pm, Sun 10.30 pm; closed Sun L.

Ekachai £17 ★

Southside Shopping Cntr, SW18 8871 3888 10–2B
9-10 The Arcade, Liverpool St, EC2 7626 1155 9–2D

High-quality fast-food at bargain prices is in short supply in the City. But a meal at this Chinese/Malaysian canteen fits the bill with its fantastic, fresh noodles and curries (typically about £8), washed down perhaps with a Singha beer (£3) or house wine (£13.50 a bottle). It also has a lesser-known sibling in Wandsworth. / www.ekachai.net; EC2 10 pm - SW18 10 pm, Fri & Sat 10.30 pm; EC2 closed Sat & Sun; minimum £10; minimum 3 people, dinner only.

The Electric Birdcage SW1 £17 A

11 Haymarket 7839 2424 4–4A

This comfortable-verging-on-lavish bar makes the best of a difficult site, right in the heart of Theatreland. Dim sum is central to a menu of Oriental bites, most of which come in between £3-£5 (and are better than just provisions to soak up alcohol). Drinks, though, aren't that cheap: wine starts at £15 a bottle, and a bottle of Peroni will set you back £4.50. / www.electricbirdcage.com; 10.30 pm; closed Sat L & Sun; no trainers.

sign up for the survey at hardens.com 39

Eriki NW3 £24 ★

4-6 Northways Pde, Finchley Rd   7722 0606   8–2A

With house wine for example, at £14.95 a bottle, this handy Swiss Cottage Indian, near the tube, is far from being a classic budget destination. It is, however, one of those places you can eat pretty well and, if you choose carefully, stay within our budget. They actually do lunch here for just £4.95, but sadly that's take-away only – if you want a seat, the one-course set lunch is £10.95. / www.eriki.co.uk; 10.30 pm.

Esarn Kheaw W12 £19 ★★

314 Uxbridge Rd   8743 8930   7–1B

This low-key Thai caféd (with its grungy Shepherd's Bush location and dowdy décor) is easily ignore. But its fiery northern Thai food is brilliant, and offers one of the most authentic tastes of south east Asia in town. A typical starter would be spiced papaya salad (£4.95) and you might follow it with sun-dried beef (£6.95) or more expensively a dish like grilled cat fish £9.95. House wine is just £10.50 a bottle, or drink Thai beer for £3.50. / www.esarnkheaw.co.uk; 11 pm; closed Sat L & Sun L; no Amex.

Esca SW4 £16

160a, Clapham High St   7622 2288   10–2D

This quality deli near Clapham Common tube is just the place for a superior snack. Prices, though, are not particularly bargain basement, and the best deal are the 'selection plates' which get you three veggie dishes for £7.90, or one meat and two veggie for £8.90. You might have chicken & mushroom pie with tabbouleh and Waldorf salad. Round of the meal with a baked cheesecake for £3.50. House wine is £11.95 a bottle. / www.escauk.com; 9 pm; no Amex.

Everest Inn SE3 £17

41 Tranquil Vale   8852 7872   1–4D

This Blackheath restaurant recently moved around the corner, but there seems little reason to expect any change in the quality of its Nepalese fare. An à la carte meal might comprise Gurkhali soup (a spicy broth with lamb or chicken dumplings, £3.95), followed by the Everest Machha Special (fish, with a crust of mustard and other spices, £7.95). There's also a 2-course lunch deal for £9.95. House wine is £12.95 a bottle. / www.everestinn.co.uk; 11.30 pm, Fri & Sat midnight.

Il Falconiere SW7 £21*

84 Old Brompton Rd   7589 2401   5–2B

The 3-course set lunch (£12.50) ensures that you'll stay well within budget at this well-worn, old-school South Kensington trattoria – at other times you'd spend rather over our price limit (and we wouldn't especially recommend paying the premium anyway). Starters of cured beef with avocado or rocket and parmesan salad and mains of pasta, veal, or grilled chicken are typical. Desserts are, of course, from a trolley. The house wine is £12.50 a bottle. / www.ilfalconiere.co.uk; 11 pm; closed Sun.

El Faro E14   **£22***   ★★

3 Turnberry Quay   7987 5511   11–2C

Despite its rather improbable Isle of Dogs location, this Spanish restaurant rightly has quite a name for the quality of its food, and its waterside setting makes it an especially good sunny-day destination. You'd have to stick to the tapas to stay within our price limit, but it would accommodate a couple of the standard small plates – perhaps calamares and a tortilla – plus a flan for dessert. (All the dishes cited are £5 or less, but many cost quite a lot more). House wine is £3.75 a glass. / www.el-faro.co.uk; 11 pm; closed Sun D.

Faulkner's E8   **£20**   ★★

424-426 Kingsland Rd   7254 6152   1–1D

This East End chippy has long been renowned for some of the best fish 'n' chips in the capital. It's not especially cheap, with prices ranging from £10.50 for cod up to £18.90 for Dover sole, but the quality is reliably high. You might start with scampi (£4.90), or you could leave space for the sticky toffee pudding (£3.90). House wine is £10.50 a bottle. / 10 pm; no Amex; need 8+ to book.

Fernandez & Wells   **£12**   ★

43 Lexington St, W1   7734 1546   3–2D

73 Beak St, W1   7287 2814   3–2D

You can hang with the hip media classes at these artful Soho pit stops. On 'Beak', it's more a coffee and a croissant job (or more fashionably a Portuguese pasteis de nata – custard tart – for £1.50). Deli-style 'Lexington' is bigger and more the place for a tapas-y meal. You might have a soup (changing daily, £4.25) and a salchichon (cured sausage) and Comté cheese bocadillo (fancy sarnie). Lexington is also licensed, with a short, well-chosen wine list, from £18.99. / Lexington 10 pm, Beak 7pm; Lexington, closed Sun.

54 Farringdon Road EC1   **£20***   ★

54 Farringdon Rd   7336 0603   9–1A

Mixed herb gnocchi & cep sauce rubs shoulders on the menu with Penang dhal vegetable curry, at this offbeat newcomer in Farringdon, which serves 'Malaysian and European Food' (with more of the former than the latter). Both are good, though, and most economically sampled at lunch (Monday-Friday, and the first Sunday of the month) and pre-theatre, when there are 2-course set menus for £12.95 and £11.95 respectively. House wine is £12.50 a bottle. / www.54farringdon.com; 11 pm; closed Sat L & Sun.

Fish Central EC1   **£18**   ★

149-155 Central St   7253 4970   9–1B

This superior 'evolved' chippy in the City is an excellent value option in its area. Go for lobsters and oysters if you want to stretch our budget, but otherwise there's an appetising array of fish that can be cooked to order in batter, or put under the char-grill. Starters are priced from £3.45, and a dish like roast cod will set you back £10.95. A bottle of house wine is £9.95. / www.fishcentral.co.uk; 10.30 pm, Fri & Sat 11 pm; closed Sun; no Amex.

Fish Club SW11 £18 ★★

189 St John's Hill   7978 7115   10–2C

A contemporary Battersea chippy (cum fishmonger), which has a big name for its fish (and other) dishes. It's a superior sort of place, paying proper attention to sourcing, and one of the few in this guide where you could even kick off your meal with a few native oysters (£1.75 each), before your choice of fish (from £5.45) and chips (£1.75). Wines kick off at £12.95 a bottle. / www.thefishclub.com; 10 pm, Sun 9 pm; closed Mon.

Fish Hook W4 £21* ★★

6-8 Elliott Rd   8742 0766   7–2A

Chef/patron Michael Nadra used to cook at the well-known Trompette over the road. He took over these plain, cramped Chiswick premises – previously called Fish Hoek – replaced the 'e' with an 'o', and introduced the odd meat dish onto the menu. It's quality cuisine and at night well out of budget. So at £12.50, the 2-course lunch deal is very good value: you might choose Bayonne ham with courgette fritters, followed by roast grey mullet. For an extra £2.50 you could follow it up with pain perdu with a sour cherry compote. There's an extensive wine list running from £15 a bottle. / www.fishhook.co.uk; 10.30 pm, Sun 10 pm.

Fish in a Tie SW11 £10* 𝔸

105 Falcon Rd   7924 1913   10–1C

You can always eat within our budget at this cramped but very popular bistro near Clapham Junction (although if you don't book, you'll do well to get a table). Top value, though, is to be had from the 2-course lunch (every day except Sunday) – for £5, your choice might be soup, then fishcakes, washed down with house wine at £9.95 a bottle. / 10.45 pm, Sun 11 pm; no Amex.

Five Hot Chillies HA0 £13 ★

875 Harrow Rd   8908 5900   1–1A

It's a trek to find this Indian caff on a busy road in Sudbury, and when you do the interior is pretty grungy and dated. The reason to bother is its excellent, spicy and authentic Pujnabi nosh, at low, low prices – a fish tikka main course is £4, for example, or karahi gosht (lamb curry) just £5.50. AND, you can BYO. AND there's no corkage. / 11.30 pm.

Flat White W1 £ 8 ★

17 Berwick St   7734 0370   3–2D

As you'll know, 'Flat White' is Kiwi-speak for a style of coffee, and this Soho pit stop is a caffeine addict's delight (with brews from £1.70). There's also food to help you indulge, with quality cakes (from £1.25), sarnies (from £3.50) and salads (from £5). / www.flat-white.co.uk; L only; no credit cards.

Food for Thought WC2 £13 ★

31 Neal St   7836 0239   4–2C

In an ever-changing culinary world, it's difficult not to warm to this cramped north-Covent Garden basement, accessed down a wooden staircase. It has long been a laid-back spot of note for offering a small and eclectic range of inexpensive and wholesome veggie fare, such as Thai vegetable curry (£4.70) or a quiche and salad (£7). There's also a mouth-watering selection of cakes and puddings, perhaps an almond and coconut scone (£1.70). BYO – no corkage. / 8 pm, Sun 5 pm; no credit cards; no booking.

The Forge WC2   £21*   A

14 Garrick St   7379 1531   4–3C

Theatreland restaurants have their own special atmosphere and this humming, civilised Gallic establishment near Covent Garden is one of the best of the breed. A la carte here is beyond our budget, but pre- or post -theatre (and at lunch) they offer a 2-course meal with coffee for £13.50 (3-course, £16.50). This could be penne with rocket & blue cheese, then grilled salmon with ratatouille, followed by crème brûlée. Wines start at £14.50 a bottle.
/ www.theforgerestaurant.co.uk; midnight.

The Four Seasons W2   £20   ★

84 Queensway   7229 4320   6–1C

Contrary to popular preconceptions, Bayswater is in fact the best part of town to head for if you're looking for a quality Chinese meal. This particular establishment is as brusque as many of its peers, but the food is consistently very good, and reasonably priced. With main courses starting around the £6 mark, and set menus from £15.50, you can always eat here within our price limit, especially as the house wine is just £9.80 a bottle. / 11 pm; no Amex.

The Fox EC2   £23*   A★

28 Paul St   7729 5708   9–1C

Michael Belben is still best known as the founder of the famous Eagle, but he's won quite a name for the cooking at this more recently acquired Shoreditch boozer. Its cosy upstairs dining room is the sort of place you can have a good light meal within our price range – perhaps a risotto (£9.50), followed by a pear tart and cream (£4.50) – but could also spend quite a lot more if you tried. Wines kick off at £13.50 a bottle. / www.thefoxpublichouse.com; 11 pm, Fri & Sat midnight; closed Sat L & Sun D; no Amex.

Franco Manca SW9   £10   ★★

Unit 4 Market Row   7738 3021   10–2D

The effort to import a wood-burning stove all the way from Naples hasn't been wasted at this new pizzeria in atmospheric Brixton Market (on the site that was Eco, RIP): the resulting sourdough pizza is magic. It helps that prices are so keen it feels like you've travelled back in time: the pizzas are about £5, with house wine costing just £6.80 for a 750cl carafe or £1.20 a small glass.
/ www.francomanca.com; L only, closed Sun; no Amex.

Frantoio SW10   £22*   A★

397 King's Rd   7352 4146   5–3B

A World's End trattoria with quite a local following. It's well outside our price range à la carte, but offers a 2-course set lunch menu (£14.50), from which your selection might be fettuccini ragu, followed by grilled chicken with pine nuts, washed down with house wine at £12.50 a bottle. / 11.15 pm.

Fratelli la Bufala NW3   £15*   ★

45a South End Rd   7435 7814   8–2A

An offshoot of a family-run operation which really is based in Italy, this pizza, pasta and so on stand-by offers a characterfully rustic experience – certainly by South Hampstead standards! You would tend to spend a little beyond our price limit à la carte, but this can make a handy lunch venue, when two courses will set you back £9.50, washed down by house wine at £13.50 a bottle. / 11 pm; closed Mon L; no Amex.

Frederick's N1   £21*   A★

106 Camden Pas   7359 2888   8–3D

This Islington veteran is one of the most charming to qualify for inclusion in this guide, and comes complete with a beautiful garden/conservatory and smart front bar. At night, you could spend a lot here, but at lunch you can enjoy two courses and coffee for just £14 – perhaps soup, then salmon with new potatoes. The extensive wine list kicks off at £17 a bottle. / www.fredericks.co.uk; 11 pm; closed Sun; no Amex.

Fresco W2   £ 8   ★

25 Westbourne Grove   7221 2355   6–1C

This small Bayswater café is a gem of a cheap eat, especially if you like freshly squeezed juices, available here at £4.95 for a litre (£2.95 for a cup). Food-wise, there's a selection of small mezze and other Middle Eastern classics – falafels are £3.25; a chicken kebab is £3.50. / www.frescojuices.co.uk; 11 pm.

La Fromagerie Café W1   £18   ★

2-4 Moxon St   7935 0341   3–1A

Patricia Michelson's cheese is arguably London's best, and her Marylebone deli has helped the area become the foodie 'destination' it is today (which is to say a remarkable one for London, but one which would pass without comment in almost any Parisian arrondissement). A small cheese plate with bread and butter will set you back £8.75, and there is quite a range of soups, salads and so on from about the same price point. Easy on the vino, though – a 125ml glass will cost you £3.95. / www.lafromagerie.co.uk; 7.30 pm, Sat 7 pm, Sun 6 pm; L only; no booking.

Fryer's Delight WC1   £ 8   ★

19 Theobald's Rd   7405 4114   2–1D

With its Formica and fluorescent strips, this Bloomsbury parlour is the archetypal chippy, right down to a regular cast of cabbies enjoying a 'fuel' stop. Haddock 'n' chips is £7 and a mug of tea to wash it down just 80p. No puddings to tempt you either. / 10 pm; closed Sun; no credit cards; no booking.

Fujiyama SW9   £17

5-7 Vining St   7737 2369   10–2D

This fun little café on a small lane is a good find in Brixton, not least thanks to the very reasonable prices of its wide-ranging menu. Hot food bento boxes range from £8.95-£12.95 – sushi versions are a couple of pounds more. Asahi beer comes in at £2.50 a go, or drink house wine at £11.95 a bottle. / www.newfujiyama.com; 11 pm, Fri & Sat midnight; no Amex.

Furnace N1   £ 20   ★

1 Rufus St   7613 0598   9–1D

This pizza 'n' pasta joint is one of the best cheap places to eat if you want to hang with the Hoxton trendies. Just off the Square, it's a buzzing, brick-lined spot, where most dishes are around £9, and a bottle of house wine costs £12.75. / www.hoxtonfurnace.com; 11 pm; closed Sat L & Sun; no Amex.

Fuzzy's Grub £11 ★★

6 Crown Pas, SW1   7925 2791   3–4D
96 Tooley St, SE1   7089 7590   9–4D
15 Basinghall St, Unit 1 Mason's Ave, EC2   7726 6771   9–2C
56-57 Cornhill, EC3   7621 0444   9–2C
58 Houndsditch, EC3   7929 1400   9–2D
10 Well Ct, EC4   7236 8400   9–2B
22 Carter Ln, EC4   7248 9795   9–2B
62 Fleet St, EC4   7583 6060   9–2A

*If you see Sunday roast as one of the cornerstones of modern
civilisation, this small group of simple but civilised British diners is for
you. And you can indulge every day of the week – either stuffed into
a brilliant sandwich (£4.95), or with a range of salads (£5.95). Other
traditional fare – such as steak 'n' kidney pudding, cottage or chicken
pies – costs a similar amount. Naturally they also do amazing
breakfasts. Unlicensed. / www.fuzzysgrub.com; 3 pm-4 pm; closed Sat &
Sun except SE1 & EC4; no credit cards; no booking.*

Gaby's WC2 £14

30 Charing Cross Rd   7836 4233   4–3B

*This veteran, Formica-tabled deli by Leicester Square tube makes
an ideal oasis for a quick Theatreland bite (even if it's more cheap
than it is cheerful). The top tips are the salt-beef sandwiches (£5.50)
or falafel. The latter is available as a starter in the 2-course lunch
deal (£7.50), where the main course might be meatballs with rice
or chips. House wine is £13 a bottle – no wonder the fruit juices here
are pretty popular! / midnight, Sun 10 pm; no credit cards.*

Gail's Bread £11 ★

138 Portobello Rd, W11   7460 0766   6–1B
64 Hampstead High St, NW3   7794 5700   8–1A

*Finding decent bread is surprisingly hard in London, and a bit of an
obsession for us here at Harden's. So we're all in favour of this small
chain of trendy café/bakeries, which offer a very good range of baked
goods. Breakfast is a good time to visit, when they offer a special
sandwich (£4.20) or an almond croissant (£2.20). Later in the day,
you might have the likes of a salad (£4.50) and a fruit juice (£2.80).
/ www.gailsbread.co.uk; W11 8 pm - NW3 9 pm; no booking.*

Galicia W10 £19

323 Portobello Rd   8969 3539   6–1A

*A gritty North Kensington tapas bar, which derives much of its
character from the presence of the Hispanic community (and school)
nearby. The 3-course lunch is inexpensive (£8.50), but not always
hugely authentic – a recent menu ran: soup, salmon steak, tiramisu –
so the best bet is to go for its tapas and raciones (around £5),
with house vino at £9.95 a bottle. / 11.30 pm; closed Mon.*

Gallipoli £19 Ⓐ

102 Upper St, N1   7359 0630   8–3D
107 Upper St, N1   7226 5333   8–3D
120 Upper St, N1   7359 1578   8–3D

*A few doors apart from each other, in the heart of Islington, these
cosy and friendly Turkish bistros are great value if you don't mind
a few 'rough edges' foodwise. They are permanently buzzing with
birthdays, hen nights and other gatherings. You could eat here à la
carte within our budget, but there are also set deals (three courses
at lunch for £12.95, or at dinner for £15.95). House wine is £10.95
a bottle, or drink Efes beer at £3.50 a go. / www.cafegallipoli.com;
11 pm, Fri & Sat midnight; 107 Upper St closed Mon.*

Galvin at Windows
Park Lane London Hilton Hotel W1　£25*　A★★
22 Park Ln, 28th Floor　7208 4021　3–4A

A few years ago, the celebrated Galvin brothers took over the 28th floor space of Park Lane's landmark Hilton Hotel. Amazingly, thanks to a newly-introduced bar menu, you can now lunch here within our budget. You will, however, have to be pretty careful. Book for the lunch express menu (£14.95) in the bar – it might be smoked salmon & caper berries followed by minute steak bordelaise & pommes fondant. A glass of wine (£5), a coffee (£2.50) and service will bring your bill to just £25.25! With a view like this, what's a few pence between friends? / www.galvinatwindows.com; 10.45 pm; closed Sat L & Sun D; no trainers.

Galvin Bistrot de Luxe W1　£25*　A★★
66 Baker St　7935 4007　2–1A

Chris and Jeff Galvin's swish, wood-panelled brasserie, a short walk from Baker Street tube, has quite a 'name' for its cuisine. We've turned a blind eye to the fact that their set meal (£15.50) is likely to lead you a fraction beyond our price limit, because it's a fabulous deal (and one that gives you three courses to boot). A typical choice would be pork rillettes, followed by grilled mackerel, with roast beetroot & horseradish butter, followed by rice pudding & caramelised figs. A small carafe (250ml) of the house wine is £5.50. / www.galvinrestaurants.com; 11 pm, Sun 9. 30 pm.

Ganapati SE15　£18　A★
38 Holly Grove　7277 2928　1–4C

This funky south Indian diner is a star in the culinary void of Peckam. For lunch, dishes like masala dosa or chicken curry are about a fiver. Evening à la carte might bust our budget, unless you go for a thali (£7.95-£12.95). There's a good selection of drinks, with lassis for £2.25, beers around £3 and wine from £13.50 a bottle. / www.ganapatirestaurant.com; 10.45 pm; closed Mon; no Amex.

The Gaylord E14　£16
141 Manchester Rd　7538 0393　11–2D

If it wasn't on the Isle of Dogs, this low key Indian might not rate mention. Given the absence of local alternatives, however, it's worth knowing about a quality curry house – albeit one in a fairly tried and tested vein. An à la carte meal is easily achieved within budget, with a classic like rogan josh costing £5.25. A bottle of house wine costs £10.95. / www.gaylordrestaurant.co.uk; midnight.

Geeta NW6　£16　★★
57-59 Willesden Ln　7624 1713　1–1B

What this grim-looking Kilburn veteran lacks in looks (a lot!) it makes up for somewhat with the smiley service of the family who run it, and prices for its home-cooked Indian dishes which are as cheap as chips: starters are £2.50-£3.50 and mains from £4.50-£7.90 (for tandoori king prawns). A bottle of Cobra is £3.50, or if you're willing to hazard the house vino it's just £1.60 a glass. / 10.30 pm, Fri & Sat 11.30 pm; no Amex.

Gem　£14　A★
265 Upper St, N1　7359 0405　8–2D
22 North St, SW4　7720 0091　10–2D

These simple Kurdish pit stops are most notable for their barbecue meat and their notably good, freshly baked bread. You'd be hard pushed to bust our budget at either of them, especially at lunchtime when there are 4-course deals for £6.95 and £8.95. House wine is £12.45 a bottle. / www.gemrestaurant.org.uk.

The Giaconda Dining Room WC2   £25*   ★
9 Denmark St   7240 3334   4–1A
*Right in the heart of town, by Centre Point, this cramped newcomer
is one of the leaders in London's new wave of quality bistros. As this
is 'real' food, though, you're going to have to stick to the cheaper end
of the menu to stay within budget – perhaps baked mushrooms with
garlic (£5.50), followed by fishcakes and green salad (£9.50).
NB There is a £1 cover charge, and wine prices kick off at £19
a bottle. / www.giacondadining.com; 9.30 pm; closed Sat & Sun.*

Glaisters SW10   £22   Ⓐ
4 Hollywood Rd   7352 0352   5–3B
*The best features of this popular Chelsea bistro are its consistency,
its lovely rear conservatory, and its modest prices for the area (house
wine, for example, is only £12). Lunch is cheaper than dinner,
with two courses for £13.50, and three courses for £15.50. You might
have tomato and mozzarella salad, rib eye steak with chips, and –
if you've gone the whole hog – chocolate tart to finish.
/ www.glaisters.co.uk; 11.30 pm; closed Sun D.*

Golden Dragon W1   £22
28-29 Gerrard St   7734 2763   4–3A
*On Chinatown's bewildering main drag, it can be hard to sift good
options from bad, but this hectic, well-established fixture is one of the
safer bets. Even à la carte you could squeeze a meal in here
(and that is probably a better course than ordering one of the
hackneyed set options, from £14.50). Best of all, though, is lunchtime
dim sum. Drink Tsingtao beer at £3.30 a bottle. / midnight.*

Golden Hind W1   £12   ★★
73 Marylebone Ln   7486 3644   2–1A
*Nothing fancy: just a knock-out, honest-to-goodness chippy with lovely
service that's within easy striking distance of the West End – it's in
Marylebone. A portion of haddock is £7.70 and chips are £1.70. The
setting is basic, but there is the option to BYO. / 10 pm; closed
Sat L & Sun.*

Good Earth   £19*   Ⓐ★
233 Brompton Rd, SW3   7584 3658   5–2C
143-145 The Broadway, NW7   8959 7011   1–1B
*As Knightsbridge is not exactly flush with budget lunching possibilities,
it's particularly worth knowing about the 2-course set lunch (£11.50)
at this smart and comfortable Chinese (whose Mill Hill sibling is also
of note as the best place to eat for miles around). You might choose
steamed dumplings, then beef in black bean sauce. House wine
is £16 a bottle, or a Tsingtao is £3.30. / www.goodearthgroup.co.uk;
10.45 pm.*

Gopal's of Soho W1   £17
12 Bateman St   7434 1621   4–2A
*Not much changes at this stalwart Soho Indian, which has long been
one of the West End's curiously few decent traditional curry houses.
A typical starter is Kaleja (chicken liver, £3.50) – a main dish like
Mangalorean mutton curry comes in at £6.95. Drink a large Cobra
for £4.60, or house wine is a modest £10.50 a bottle (as it has been
for years). / www.gopalsofsoho.co.uk; 11.30 pm.*

sign up for the survey at hardens.com   47

Gordon's Wine Bar WC2 £18 A

47 Villiers St 7930 1408 4–4D

For atmosphere alone, it's hard to better this well-known wine bar near Embankment tube, with its ancient candlelit vaults and its vast outside terrace for summer drinking. A well-chosen wine list, from £13.50 a bottle, is much of the appeal, plus a tempting array of sherries, ports and Madeiras. The food is adequate: there's a daily selection of hot dishes with salad (£7-£10), plus a cold selection of which the cheese-platters (from £7.60) have their fans.
/ www.gordonswinebar.com; 11 pm, Sun 10 pm; no booking.

Gourmet Burger Kitchen £15 ★

15 Frith St, W1 7494 9533 4–2A
13-14 Maiden Ln, WC2 7240 9617 4–4D
163-165 Earl's Court Rd, SW5 7373 3184 5–2A
49 Fulham Broadway, SW6 7381 4242 5–4A
107 Old Brompton Rd, SW7 7581 8942 5–2B
160 Portobello Rd, W11 7243 6597 6–1B
50 Westbourne Grove, W2 7243 4344 6–1B
131 Chiswick High Rd, W4 8995 4548 7–2A
200 Haverstock Hill, NW3 7443 5335 8–2A
44 Northcote Rd, SW11 7228 3309 10–2C
333 Putney Bridge Rd, SW15 8789 1199 10–2B
84 Clapham High St, SW4 7627 5367 10–2D
Condor Hs, St Paul's Churchyard, EC4 7248 9199 9–2B

Burgers every which way – 'Cajun' for instance at £7.25 – have made this now ubiquitous chain of diners the capital's benchmark for burger-lovers, despite their decidedly unlovely premises. Rounding off your order with a side of fat chips will set you back an extra £2.70. A Steinlager is £3.30 for a bottle, wine £11.95, or opt for a yummy shake (£3.50). / www.gbkinfo.com; 10.45 pm; no booking.

Govinda's W1 £11 ★

9 Soho St 7437 4928 4–1A

For a filling West End snack at bargain prices, it's hard to beat the cafeteria adjoining the Hare Krishna temple, just off Soho Square. For religious reasons, meat, onions and garlic don't feature in dishes, but that doesn't stop them from being hearty and tasty, and the place draws a nicely eclectic crowd. The best budget bets are the set meals (£7.95 or less, served noon-8pm) which consist of two rices, steamed vegetables, dahl, salad, naan and poppadoms. Alcohol and caffeine are also proscribed, so you will have to stick with a lassi (£1.60) or herbal tea (£1.50). / www.iskcon-london.org; 8 pm; closed Sun; no Amex.

The Gowlett SE15 £18 A★

62 Gowlett Rd 7635 7048 1–4C

A focus on pizza makes this Peckham boozer that rare beast – a really affordable gastropub – and locals love its easy style and good nosh (salads for about a fiver, pizzas around £9). You could drink house wine at £11, but that would be a waste given its award-winning, and ever-changing selection of real ales. / www.thegowlett.com; 10.30 pm.

Great Nepalese NW1   £16   ★

48 Eversholt St   7388 6737   8–3C

The location is grotty – down the side of Euston Station – and yet this friendly curry house has maintained a loyal fan club for many years. Friendly service helps, as do affordable, well-made dishes with quite a few Nepalese specials. To really pare costs, seek out the 2-course lunch for £6.95: it might be an onion bhaji then chicken Kashmiri. House wine is £10.75 a bottle. / www.great-nepalese.co.uk; 11.30 pm; closed Sun.

Green & Blue SE22   £16   𝔸

38 Lordship Ln   8693 9250   1–4D

You don't drop in to this bar attached to an East Dulwich merchants for the food – the fare such as taramasalata (£3.50) or tuna panini (£6.50) are fine, but not the main point. The scoff is there to help you sample their fabulous wine selection, which won the shop 'Best UK Small Independent' in the Decanter wine awards. The least expensive on their list is provided at £3.50 a glass or £11.75 a bottle. There's now also a branch in Clapham.
/ www.greenandbluewines.com; 11 pm, Fri & Sat midnight, Sun 10.30 pm; no Amex.

Greig's W1   £19*   ★

26 Bruton Pl   7629 5613   3–2B

Tucked-away in a cute mews, this long-established Mayfair steakhouse is far from being a natural cheap eat. Stick to the keenly-priced lunch deal, though, and you can eat in this plush joint within budget. Two courses are £9.95, three £12.95 – you might have mixed salad, then cottage pie, with chocolate mousse to finish. Given the location, house wine is reasonably priced, at £14.95 a bottle. / www.greigs.com; midnight.

Ground W4   £16   𝔸★

219-221 Chiswick High Rd   8747 9113   7–2A

It's always a pleasure to see a simple idea executed well, as it is at this Chiswick burger café. It's like GBK – just better, especially on the décor front. Dishes really hit their mark, with a fancier option like the Hawaiian burger coming in at £7.80. The salads (around a fiver) are perfectly good, if not the point. A pint of draught Red Stripe is £3.60, or drink wine at £12.95 a bottle. / www.groundrestaurants.com; Sun-Mon 10 pm, Tue-Thu 10.30 pm, Fri & Sat 11 pm.

Gung-Ho NW6   £23   ★

328-332 West End Ln   7794 1444   1–1B

A local favourite, this stylish West Hampstead Chinese offers a friendly welcome, as well as decent fare. It would be easy to overspend, but choose carefully and it's not too hard to keep within our budget – you might have smoked chicken shreds (£5.50) with fried rice (£4) followed by toffee apple or banana (£2.80). House wine is £12.50 a bottle. / www.stir-fry.co.uk; 11.30 pm; no Amex.

Haandi SW3   £20*   ★

7 Cheval Pl   7823 7373   5–1C

For somewhere almost opposite Harrod's (hidden away in a mews), this quality curry house is notably reasonably priced. Wine is quite expensive, though, at £14.95 a bottle, and if you dine here à la carte, you might have difficulty staying within our price limit. The one-course lunch deal (£9.95), however, offers an excellent respite from shopping. / www.haandi-restaurants.com; 11 pm, Fri-Sat 11.30 pm.

Haché £19 ★

329-331 Fulham Rd, SW10   7823 3515   5–3B
24 Inverness St, NW1   7485 9100   8–3B
In Camden Town, and now Chelsea, this rather upmarket-feeling
bistro mini-chain has made quite a name for the quality of its burgers
(around £8, with frites for £2 on top). House wine is £12.95 a bottle,
so you can indulge in a chocolate brownie (£4.95) too, and still stay
comfortably within our budget.

Hamburger Union £14 ★

25 Dean St, W1   7437 6004   4–2A
64 Tottenham Court Rd, W1   7636 0011   2–1C
4-6 Garrick St, WC2   7379 0412   4–3C
Irving St (off Leicester Sq), WC2   7839 8100   4–4B
341 Upper St, N1   7359 4436   8–3D
Offering standards roughly comparable to the larger Gourmet Burger
Kitchen chain, this good-quality multiple offers decent burgers
(from about £4) and salads (from about £3). For maximum
authenticity, milkshakes are £2.95, or house wine is £12.95 a bottle.
/ 10.30 pm; no booking, except N1 upstairs room.

Hammersmith Café W6 £13 ★

1a Studland St   8748 2839   7–2B
A greasy spoon by day, this grungy caff near Hammersmith Town
Hall goes Thai in the evening, and makes a cheap but dependable
refuelling stop. Mixed starters will set you back £6.60 – for two,
that is – with most curries weighing in at around a fiver. You can BYO
– corkage is £2 per bottle. / 10.30 pm; closed Sun; no Amex.

Haozhan W1 £22 ★

8 Gerrard St   7434 3838   4–3A
There's been something of a wind of change blowing through
Chinatown in recent years, and this 'modern Oriental' dining room
is one of the better new arrivals. For the very best value, go for the
excellent set lunchtime menu, when £8 might buy you the likes
of won ton soup and Singapore noodles, washed down with wines
starting off at £13.50 a bottle. If you choose reasonably carefully,
though, you could dine here within our price limit at any time.
/ www.haozhan.co.uk; 11.30 pm, Fri & Sat midnight, Sun 11 pm.

Harbour City W1 £15

46 Gerrard St   7439 7859   4–3B
The décor may be rather understated by local standards, but this
Chinatown spot still attracts a faithful following. It's at lunchtime
(noon-5pm) that people particularly seek the place out for its notably
interesting selection of dim sum, when nothing costs more than £3.
A bottle of Tsingtao beer is £2.20. / 11.30 pm, Fri & Sat midnight,
Sun 10.

Hare & Tortoise £15 ★

15-17 Brunswick Sq, WC1   7278 4945   2–1D
38 Haven Grn, SW5   8610 7066   1–2A
373 Kensington High St, W14   7603 8887   7–1D
296-298 Upper Richmond Rd, SW15   8394 7666   10–2B
No wonder there's often a queue for these bright pan-Asian cafés.
OK, they're a bit chainy, but portions are generous, prices are keen,
and quality is impressively consistent – especially given the wide-
ranging nature of a menu incorporating sushi, ramen (noodles) and
rice dishes. A 10-piece sushi box is £7.50, or pork mis ramen
is £5.75. Kirin beer is £3.90 per pint.
/ www.hareandtortoise-restaurants.co.uk; 10.45 pm; W14 no bookings.

The Hartley SE1   £20   ★

64 Tower Bridge Rd   7394 7023   1–3C

In the culinary wasteland a mile or so to the south of Tower Bridge, this no-nonsense gastropub is a deserved success. The menu is fairly wide-ranging, price-wise, and you'd have to stick to the cheaper items to stay comfortably within our budget – perhaps bruschetta with goat's cheese (£4.50) followed by fishcake & chips (£8), washed down with house wine at £12.95 a bottle. / www.thehartley.com; 10 pm, Sun 7 pm.

Haz   £20

9 Cutler St, E1   7929 7923   9–2D

6 Mincing Ln, EC3   7929 3173   9–3D

These stylish Turkish restaurants in the City really don't look like budget affairs. Thanks to their good quality and reasonable prices, they are often packed. Mixed mezze (£6.45 per person) is the standard starter, and there are a good number of main courses around the £8 mark (although you can pay more). Wines kick off at £13.25 a bottle. / www.hazrestaurant.co.uk; 11.30 pm.

Hazuki WC2   £16*   ★

43 Chandos Pl   7240 2530   4–4C

Handy for much of Theatreland, this welcoming Japanese restaurant by the Trafalgar Square post office is worth knowing about, both lunchtime and evening. Midday menus really are very reasonably priced, with a fair variety of offers for under a tenner, assuring considerable local popularity. By night, you'd have to pick pretty carefully to stay within budget, but with set menus from £16, and house wine at £13.50 a bottle, it's perfectly possible. / www.hazukilondon.co.uk; 10.30 pm, Sun 9.30 pm; closed Sun L

Hellenik W1   £23   A★

30 Thayer St   7935 1257   2–1A

If you were looking for a film set for London in the '60s, it would be hard to better this wonderfully unchanging Greek institution in Marylebone, where charming service is a particular strength. You'll need to choose reasonably carefully to stay within our price limit – you might have houmous (£4.50) followed by moussaka with salad (£11.75) – but it is perfectly possible. The house wine is £11 a bottle. / 10.45 pm; closed Sun; no Amex.

High Road Brasserie W4   £21*   A★

162-166 Chiswick High Rd   8742 7474   7–2A

If you want to hang out with the west London media crowd, this outpost of the empire of Nick Jones (best known for the club Soho House) is the place to do it. Perhaps unsurprisingly, it's outside our price range generally speaking, so the two-course set lunch menu (£12) is especially worth remembering – your selection might be smoked trout & beetroot salad followed by grey mullet & samphire, washed down with house wine at £10 a bottle. / www.highroadhouse.co.uk; 10.45 pm, Fri & Sat 11.45 pm.

Hilliard EC4   £18   A★★

26a Tudor St   7353 8150   9–3A

This odd but admirable outfit nestles by one of the gates to the Temple (where barristers have their chambers). And it's not only thanks to the impressive range of wines (from £14 a bottle) on offer that it's very popular with the local legal folk. The food, which aims to make the best use of good seasonal ingredients, really is very good indeed. Soups and tarts are sub-£4, and a roast and tatties somewhere round a tenner. / 7 pm; closed Sat & Sun.

Hot Stuff SW8 £ 8 A★★

19 Wilcox Rd   7720 1480   10–1D

The Vauxhall streetscape outside this tiny BYO caff was the backdrop to Daniel Day Lewis's first big screen hit: 'My Beautiful Launderette'. Nowadays, though, it's a place of pilgrimage for curry fans, thanks to this absolutely brilliant bargain-basement curry-stop. Typical dishes include chilli paneer at £3.60 or garlic & chilli king prawns for £6.50. Much of the life of the place comes from its friendly host, Raj. / www.eathotstuff.com; 10 pm; closed Sun.

Hoxton Apprentice N1 £ 17

16 Hoxton Sq   7749 2828   9–1D

This enthusiastic Hoxton project for the disadvantaged may not aim that high in terms of gastronomy, but nor does it charge top dollar, especially if you go for the 2-course set lunch for £9.99. How well you do – in terms of the service or the food – is something of a lottery, but that's all part of the fun of a visit. House wine is £12.95 a bottle. / www.hoxtonapprentice.com; 11 pm.

Hummus Bros £ 12 ★

88 Wardour St, W1   7734 1311   3–2D
36-67 Southampton Row, WC1   7404 7079   2–1D

For a filling cheap snack, this expanding chain is just the job… if you like hummus (and don't mind a cheek-by-jowl, canteen-style environment). Every dish comes with hummus round the outside of the plate, while the central serving changes. Options include guacamole, chicken, daal and so on, for about a fiver. You also get pitta. Branches are unlicensed, so get virtuous with an Innocent smoothie or a hot spiced apple juice for a couple of quid. / www.hbros.co.uk; 10 pm, Thu Fri Sat 11pm; WC1 closed Sat & Sun; no bookings.

Huong-Viet
An Viet House N1 £ 12 ★

12-14 Englefield Rd   7249 0877   1–1C

Your classic chaotic Vietnamese canteen, occupying part of a cultural centre on the outer fringes of Islington whose spacious and characterful premises were once De Beauvoir Town's public baths. House wine here is £10 a bottle, and this is the sort of place where it's pretty much impossible to spend more than £20 a head, even if you stuff yourself. Beware the bizarre cover charge policy, though – the £1 a head charge is doubled for parties of more than six. / www.huongviet.co.uk; 11 pm; closed Sun; no Amex.

Imli W1 £ 17 ★

167-169 Wardour St   7287 4243   3–1D

Modern Indian tapas is the successful concept at this large, quite stylish Soho three-year-old (with swish basement cocktail bar) – an affordable and healthy central pit stop. Most dishes are in the £4-£6 range, and they also do various deals including a 3-course pre-theatre menu for £9.95. There's a wide range of drinks from healthy lassis (£3.75) to less healthy cocktails (£5.95). / www.imli.co.uk; 11 pm, Sat 11.30 pm, Sun 10 pm.

Inaho W2 £18* ★★
4 Hereford Rd   7221 8495   6–1B
*It may only be tiny, but this offbeat Bayswater shack packs a big
punch when it comes to offering great Japanese food at affordable
prices (if sometimes rather slowly). The sushi is particularly good but,
at £16 or more for a 'set', one of the pricer options. There's also
a £10 set lunch which might feature a tempura dish as the
'main event'. House wine is £11 a bottle, or a Sapporo is £3. / 11 pm;
closed Sat L & Sun; no Amex or Maestro.*

Inamo W1 £23 𝔸
134-136 Wardour St   7851 7051   3–1D
*What this Soho Japanese lacks in culinary finesse it makes up for
with fun gimmickry – in particular that you: i) order online from your
touch screen tabletop; and ii) get to control the pattern projected
onto it. While you're fiddling around with all that, you can enjoy a 2-
course meal starting from £15 (perhaps pomegranate duck with miso
soup, followed by mango and stick rice). House wine is £14 a bottle.
/ www.inamo-restaurant.com.*

India Club
Strand Continental Hotel WC2 £15
143 Strand   7836 0650   2–2D
*This curious scruffy gem of a cheap eat – a Formica-tabled canteen,
up two flights of stairs in an hotel near Aldwych – owes half a century
in business to the proximity of the Indian High Commission. Basic
curries come at bargain-basement prices (from £3.70-£5). Unlicensed
– BYO, or fetch a drink from the hotel bar. / 10.45 pm; no credit cards;
booking: max 6.*

Indian Ocean SW17 £18 ★
216 Trinity Rd   8672 7740   10–2C
*It's nothing remarkable to look at, but this large and comfortable
Wandsworth subcontinental is a notably welcoming place, and has
long done what it does with impressive consistency. Curries are
around the £6.50 mark, and a bottle of Cobra will set you back
£4.50. / 11.30 pm.*

Indian Zing W6 £22 𝔸★★
236 King St   8748 5959   7–2B
*Manog Vasaikar's Indian two-year-old in Hammersmith is making
quite a name for its accomplished cooking. It doesn't look at all
cheap – the interior is smart and service is notably good – but our
budget can accommodate eating here at any time, thanks to a fair
number of à la carte main courses for under a tenner. It's
easiest at lunch, though, when the 2-course set menu will set you
back just £12. Drink a lassi for £4. / www.indianzing.co.uk; 10.30 pm.*

Inshoku SE1 £13
23-24 Lower Marsh   7928 2311   9–4A
*This busy and authentic Japanese restaurant is an ever-popular stand-
by for those passing through Waterloo. You can eat here within our
budget at any time, but top value is to be had from the lunchtime set
menus, which include bento boxes for around £7, washed down with
house wine at £9 a bottle. / 10.30 pm; closed Sat L & Sun.*

Itsu £18 ★

103 Wardour St, W1 7479 4790 3–2D
118 Draycott Ave, SW3 7590 2400 5–2C
Level 2, Cabot Place East, E14 7512 5790 11–1C
By the standards of conveyor-sushi chains, these stylish joints – part-owned by Pret-founder Julian Metcalfe – hold up well in terms of the consistency of their 'offer', and make a buzzy and fun option for a light meal. For pre-made sushi you pay per plate (typically £4-£5). Fancier 'hand rolls' or grilled dishes (like tiger prawn tempura, £6.95) are delivered to order. House wine is £14.95 a bottle. / www.itsu.co.uk; 11 pm, E14 10 pm; Cabot Pl closed Sun; no booking.

Izgara N3 £13

11 Hendon Lane 8371 8282 1–1B
Finchley isn't over-blessed with good quality locals, making it all the more worth knowing about this popular Turkish café/takeaway. We've decided to list it even though they won't confirm any menu prices over the phone, or fax us the menu as they keep promising! All we can tell you, then, is that our annual survey still rates the place favourably, and that our recollection is that everything here is pretty cheap. / midnight; no Amex.

Jashan HA0 £10 ★★

1-2 Coronet Pde, Ealing Rd 8900 9800 1–1A
If you haven't booked, expect to queue at this no-frills (but very professionally run) Wembley canteen. The menus, veggie only, offer an enormous choice, but all of good quality – you might have the likes of chilli paneer (£4.75) followed by tandoori lamb (£4.50) and rice (£2.25). They serve fresh juices for £2.75 a glass. / 10.30 pm; no Amex; need 6+ to book, Sat & Sun.

Jenny Lo's Tea House SW1 £13 ★★

14 Eccleston St 7259 0399 2–4B
Noodles, noodles and more noodles (£6.95-£8.50) are the main offering at this small and welcoming parlour, not far from Victoria Station, run by Jenny Lo, the daughter of Ken Hom, Britain's most prolific Chinese cookery writer. Wash them down with house wine at £12.50 a bottle or a Tsingtao beer for £2.75. / 10 pm; closed Sat L & Sun; no credit cards; no booking.

Jin Kichi NW3 £18 ★★

73 Heath St 7794 6158 8–1A
Since way before the cuisine became ubiquitous, this crammed but friendly operation, in the heart of Hampstead, has been dispensing brilliant, cheap Japanese dishes. Yakitori is a good here (skewers are typically a couple of pounds), as is the sushi (a 7-piece set is £14.80), and a large menu of other items. A hot sake is £3.40, or drink oolong tea for £1.80 a cup. / www.jinkichi.com; 11 pm, Sun 10 pm; closed Mon, Tue-Fri D only, Sat & Sun open L & D.

Joy King Lau WC2 £18 ★

3 Leicester St 7437 1132 4–3A
This large Chinatown classic may look average, but it's distinguished by its consistently good cooking. Lunchtime dim sum – all dishes under £3 – is the most notable part of the operation, but the à la carte menu (most dishes around £7) is also well realised. House wine is £11 a bottle, or drink tea (50p). / 11.30 pm.

Just Falafs £12 ★

155 Wardour St, W1   7734 1914   3–1D
27b Covent Garden Piazza, WC2   7240 3838   4–3D

Standards can be a bit up-and-down, but – on a good day – you get truly delicious wraps (especially with falafel, £4.75) at this small and very informal chain, whose Covent Garden branch has cute outside tables at the end of the market. Drinks tend to be of the likes of juices or green tea, for around a couple of pounds.
/ www.justfalafs.com; WC2 8 pm, W1 9 pm; W1 closed Sun; no Amex.

K10 EC2 £16 ★

20 Copthall Ave   7562 8510   9–2C

Creative cuisine and efficient service have combined to make this City conveyor-belt sushi restaurant extremely popular. Dishes are relatively modestly priced (£2-£5.25). This is the sort of place you might want to drink beer (Asahi, £3.30), though – wines kick off at a rather surprising £18.95 a bottle. / www.k10.net; L only, closed Sat & Sun; no booking.

Kandoo W2 £14 ★

458 Edgware Rd   7724 2428   8–4A

Near Lord's, this unpretentious spot offers competent cooking at notably affordable prices – perhaps chicken on the bone (£8), followed by Persian ice cream (£2.80). Bills are kept well under control by the fact that this is strictly a BYO place (and with no corkage). / www.kandoorestaurant.co.uk; midnight.

Karma W14 £18 ★

44 Blythe Rd   7602 9333   7–1D

This tricky, out-of-the-way corner site behind Olympia has seen many excellent restaurants fail. Let's hope that's not a fate to befall this latest incumbent: an exemplary modern Indian with charming service. You could eat here any time within our budget, but the 2-course lunch is a particular bargain at just £11.95. The short wine list – superior for an Indian – kicks off at £13.95, or drink Cobra or Kingfisher for £2.70 a 330ml bottle. / www.k-a-r-m-a.co.uk; 11.30 pm; no Amex.

Kastoori SW17 £20 ★★

188 Upper Tooting Rd   8767 7027   10–2C

Sensational East African-influenced vegetarian cooking at low prices has long made this family-run Tooting shop-conversion one of London's top Indian restaurants. 'Thali' set lunch menus (around £9) are a particular bargain, and, à la carte, most dishes are under £7. For a subcontinental there's an unusually good range of wines too, kicking off at £10.95 a bottle. / 10.30 pm; closed Mon L & Tue L; no Amex or Maestro; booking: max 12.

Kasturi EC3 £22

57 Aldgate High St   7480 7402   9–2D

On the eastern fringe of the City, this smart restaurant is a handy destination if you're in search of quality subcontinental fare at reasonable prices. Some dishes – such as dahi machili (talapia fish in a chilli sauce, £9.95) – are slightly out-of-the-ordinary too. The house wine is £14.95 a bottle. / www.kasturi-restaurant.co.uk; 11 pm, Sat 9.30 pm.

sign up for the survey at hardens.com

Kazan £18*

93-94 Wilton Rd, SW1   7233 7100   2–4B
34-36 Houndsditch, EC3   7626 2222   9–2D

No disrespect to the new east-City operation, but it's the buzzy Pimlico branch – five minutes' walk from Victoria – which makes this dynamic Turkish duo of some note. In, admittedly, a surprisingly thin area, it's usually packed. This is the sort of place where you could, with care, always dine within our price limit. At lunch, however, it is a breeze, and two courses – the first a good mixed mezze – will set you back £11.95. The house wine is £14.50 a bottle.

Kensington Square Kitchen W8 £18

9 Kensington Sq   7938 2598   5–1A

Despite its no-nonsense name, this is a rather 'girly' all-day café, aimed at ladies-who-lunch, and Ken High Street shoppers looking for a comfortable place to treat themselves with breakfast (most dishes around £6), or good home-made cake (£3) and coffee (£2.50). For lunch, there's a good range of sandwiches, salads, and other light dishes (mainly £6-£10). Wines from £3.75 a glass. (Tip: the basement is more atmospheric than the ground floor.)
/ www.kensingtonsquarekitchen.co.uk; 6 pm; closed Sun.

(Brew House)
Kenwood House NW3 £18   Ⓐ

Hampstead Heath   8341 5384   8–1A

A steady stream of locals and tourists ensure that this cafe attached to Hampstead Heath's magnificent Kenwood House is always buzzing. Start the day with a top-quality full breakfast (£7.25), or in the afternoon, you might have a pot of tea (£1.50) and a treacle tart (£1.75). A lunch dish from the buffet selection – perhaps free-range sausages with vegetables of the day – will set you back about £8. Try to visit in fine weather when you can sit in the beautiful garden.
/ www.companyofcooks.com; 6 pm (summer), 4 pm (winter).

Khan's W2 £16   ★

13-15 Westbourne Grove   7727 5420 · 6–1C

The cavernous interior may evoke an Indian railway station, but this Bayswater stalwart is still a top choice for a cheap and decent curry (mostly around £7). Best of all, booze is off-limits, so this can end up being a very cheap eat indeed. / www.khansrestaurant.com; 11.45 pm.

Khan's of Kensington SW7 £20   ★

3 Harrington Rd   7584 4114   5–2B

What to say about this 'plain vanilla' South Kensington curry house? It's of note for being not too pricey, and consistently good at what it does. Papri chaat (£4.95) might be your starter, followed perhaps by a chicken & mushroom sashlik £8.95. House wine is £10.95 a bottle. / www.khansofkensington.co.uk; 11 pm.

Khoai £12   ★

362 Ballards Ln, N12   8445 2039   1–1B
6 Topsfield Pde, N8   8341 2120   1–1C

The Crouch End original of this duo of Vietnamese cafés nowadays has a bright, modern sibling that's one of the few decent eating options in North Finchley. Their vibrant cooking comes at an extremely affordable price, with main dishes in the £5-£10 range (or to really cut costs, go for the 1- or 2-course lunch deal at £4.99/£7.45). A bottle of Hue beer is £3, or there's wine from £10 a bottle.

Kipferl EC1 £13
70 Long Ln 7796 2229 9–1B
Overlooking Smithfield Market, this small deli/café is the London home of such Austrian specialities as Sachertorte (£3.50), and a very decent cup of Viennese coffee (£2) to go with it. There are also savoury specialities, though, such as Frittaten soup with pancake strips (£3.20). / www.kipferl.co.uk; L only, closed Sun.

Knaypa W6 £20 ★
268 King St 8563 2887 7–2B
This new venture, near Ravenscourt Park tube, may confirm your prejudices about Polish food, but it's a winning, sort of place, when it comes to good value. With starters such as kulebiak (cheese pasty, £4.50) and main courses such as pancakes and pierogi for under a tenner, you can easily fill up within our budget here, even if you could also bust it with the pricier dishes. For lunch, a large meaty platter comes with a non-alcoholic drink for £9.95. For drinks value, quaff draft Zywiec at £3.30 a pint. / www.theknaypa.co.uk; 11 pm.

Koba W1 £23* Ⓐ★★
11 Rathbone St 7580 8825 2–1C
Just off Charlotte Street, this stylish joint is one of the capital's more inviting Koreans, and a good place to sample this relatively little-known cuisine. Lunch is the most affordable time to visit, with 20 or so options ranging from £6 (for rice and noodle dishes) to £10.80 (for something from the BBQ). Wine options start at a hefty £15.90 a bottle, so beers (from around £3) may be preferred. / www.koba-london.com; 11 pm; closed Sun L.

Kolossi Grill EC1 £18
56-60 Rosebery Ave 7278 5758 9–1A
This old war horse in Clerkenwell may be a '60s throwback, but for a taverna experience – enlivened by characterful long-serving staff – it's a classic. You'll find it hard to over-spend here, especially if you go for the 3-course lunch for £5.50! (You might have taramasalata with pitta, meatballs with salad & rice, then fresh fruit to finish.) House wine is £12.95 a bottle. / www.kolossigrill.com; 11 pm; closed Sat L & Sun.

Konditor & Cook £9 ★
99 Shaftesbury Ave, W1 7292 1684 4–3A
46 Gray's Inn Rd, WC1 7404 6300 9–1A
30 St Mary Axe, EC3 0845 262 3030 9–2D
For a sinful snack, the irresistible cakes and other treats (around £2-£3) on offer at these wonderful cafés make a top choice. But they also do very good savouries, soups, sarnies and salads, which rarely cost more than £3 each. Drink tea (£1.25) or a smoothie (£3.25). / www.konditorandcook.com; W1 11 pm, Sun 10.30 pm, Cornwall Rd & Stoney St SE1 6pm, WC1 7pm; Cornwall Rd & Stoney St SE1 closed Sun; no booking.

Kovalam NW6 £15 ★
12 Willesden Ln 7625 4761 1–2B
Hidden away in Kilburn, an unpretentious and rather sweet Indian café, offering tasty food at bargain-basement prices. A main course of chicken Malabar, for example, will set you back all of £5.95, and house wine is £9.90 a bottle. / www.kovalamrestaurant.co.uk; 11 pm.

Kulu Kulu W1   £15   ★

76 Brewer St   7734 7316   3–2D

*Less gimmicky than many of their Kaiten-Zushi (conveyor-sushi)
competitors, these genuine Orientals concentrate on offering value
in the food department – their interior design is pretty dodgy! Prices
are not high, with sushi sets ranging from £6 for four salmon rolls
to £12.90 for a mixed 16-piece sashimi set, and noodle dishes
around £3.20. Green tea is free, and a bottle of Asahi beer is £3.20.
/ 10 pm; closed Sun; no Amex; no booking.*

Kurumaya EC4   £20   ★

76-77 Watling St   7236 0236   9–2B

*This pleasant Japanese restaurant makes a handy City lunch
(or dinner) spot, not far from St Paul's. It offers a variety of dining
options (including a tatami, shoes-off, area), and plenty of scope for
the budget diner, with many set meals available in the £9-£16.50
price range, and plenty of à la carte main dishes too. House wine
is £13.50 a bottle. / www.kurumaya.co.uk; 9.30 pm; closed Sat & Sun.*

Lahore Kebab House E1   £15   ★★

2-4 Umberston St   7488 2551   11–1A

*This no-frills dive, a short walk east of the City, is now such a Mecca
for curry-lovers that it underwent a big expansion a couple of years
ago. Its Formica-tabled, BYO appeal has survived unchanged, though,
thanks to the unvarying quality of its basic scoff – particularly the
legendary kebabs and lamb chops, with most main dishes costing
around £7. Save space for a dish like gajar jaman (carrot pudding,
£2.50). / www.lahore-kebabhouse.com; midnight; need 8+ to book.*

The Lansdowne NW1   £24*   A★

90 Gloucester Ave   7483 0409   8–3B

*This popular Primrose Hill spot – one of London's earliest gastropubs
– isn't the hot ticket it once was, but still has a big following. The cost-
saving strategy here is to stick to one of the good pizzas (mostly £9-
£10) and a pudding (£5-£6) – anything else will blow the budget.
House wine is £13.90 a bottle. / www.thelansdownepub.co.uk; 10 pm;
no Amex.*

La Lanterna SE1   £22   ★

6-8 Mill St   7252 2420   11–2A

*The purlieus of Tower Bridge are not best known for budget dining
opportunities, so this bustling, friendly and unpretentious Italian is all
the more worth knowing about (especially in summer, when you can
sit in the courtyard). This is no bargain-basement destination, but the
food – with lots of pizzas and pastas (£7.95-£12) – is of good
quality. The house wine is £13 a bottle. / www.pizzerialalanterna.co.uk;
11 pm; closed Sat L.*

Latymers W6   £16   ★

157 Hammersmith Rd   8741 2507   7–2C

*On a dreary stretch of highway between Olympia and Hammersmith,
this Fuller's gin palace doesn't seem an inviting prospect. At the back,
though, you'll find a cramped Thai dining room, which offers great
value. At lunch, one-plate dishes (around £6.25) such as pad Thai
or jungle curry with rice are the top-value choice. In the evening,
there are starters too, such as chicken satay (£3.95). Drink house
wine at £11.95 a bottle, or a pint of Carling for £3.20. / 10 pm; closed
Sun D; no Amex; no booking at L.*

Lemonia NW1 £14* Ⓐ

89 Regent's Park Rd 7586 7454 8–3B

You'll definitely need to book if you want to dine at this ever-popular, family-run taverna in Primrose Hill. You can generally just turn up on spec for lunch though, which is a particularly good time for the bargain-hunter, whether you go for the 2-course menu (£9), or the 3-course 'special' (£10.50). There's a range of Greek wines – house vino comes by the litre (£17). You might just dine here within our price limit too, but you'd need to be careful. / 11.30 pm; closed Sat L & Sun D; no Amex.

Leon £14

275 Regent St, W1 7495 1514 3–1C
35-36 Gt Marlborough St, W1 7437 5280 3–2C
73-76 The Strand, WC2 7240 3070 4–4D
136 Old Brompton Rd, SW3 7589 7330 5–1D
7 Canvey St, SE1 7620 0035 9–4B
Cabot Place West, E14 7719 6200 11–1C
3 Crispin Pl, E1 7247 4369 9–1D
12 Ludgate Circus, EC4 7489 1580 9–2A
86 Cannon St, EC4 7623 9699 9–3C

This funky chain has a lot going for it, so it's a shame that remorseless growth is blunting its once-brilliant standards. However, its junk-free snack formula still makes for a quick, healthy bite, and at night some branches become more relaxed and less 'fast foody'. Classic options include their 'superfood salad' (£5), or a 'Leon Gobi' curry (£5.80) and a cake or ice cream will set you back £3-£5. On the Strand you can BYO (no corkage), but some branches are licensed with house wine starting at £3.50 a glass. / www.leonrestaurants.co.uk; 10 pm; EC4 closed Sat & Sun, W1 closed Sun D; D only.

Lisboa Pâtisserie W10 £4 ★★

57 Golborne Rd 8968 5242 6–1A

This hip pâtisserie in North Kensington (part of a small chain) featured in the famous Vanity Fair issue that helped coin the phrase 'Cool Britannia'. It's still a hit with the area's bright young things (as well as the strong local Portuguese community), so you may face a scrum for a seat on weekends and sunny days. Its most famous attractions are the pasteis de nata (custard tarts, 80p). / 7.30 pm; L & early evening only; no booking.

Little Bay £16 Ⓐ

140 Wandsworth Bridge Rd, SW6 7751 3133 10–1B
228 Belsize Rd, NW6 7372 4699 1–2B
228 York Rd, SW11 7223 4080 10–2B
171 Farringdon Rd, EC1 7278 1234 9–1A

There's always a trade-off between quality and price, yet these madcap budget bistros leave people puzzled at just how they manage to produce 'proper' food at such amazingly low prices. Even à la carte, you can stay well within our budget. There's also a 2-course lunch deal, however, for £8.70 – you might have goat's cheese croquettes followed by breast of duck. House wine is £11.95 a bottle. / www.little-bay.co.uk; 11.30 pm; no Amex, NW6 no credit cards.

The Little Square W1 £15 ★

3 Shepherd Mkt   7355 2101   3–4B

This tiny bistro might not rate mention if it didn't enjoy one of the cutest locations in town – on a corner overlooking Shepherd Market. A la carte, you'd struggle to stay within our budget, but at the weekends they do a simple 2-course lunch for £8.50. It might comprise soup, followed by a burger with fries and salad. House wine is £3.80 a glass. / 11 pm.

Lola Rojo SW11 £19 🇦★

78 Northcote Rd   7350 2262   10–2C

Above-average tapas, with the odd contemporary twist, have made this Battersea bar a popular destination. Prices of the dishes vary widely – tapas are mainly between £2.20 and £8, and there are some main dishes for around a tenner – so the potential range of expenditures here is quite large. With wine prices kicking off in the mid-teens, though, this is clearly not the place for a budget drinking session. / http://www.lolarojo.net/; 10.30 pm.

Los Molinos W6 £20

127 Shepherd's Bush Road   7603 2229   7–1C

This cosy-looking bar sits on a corner of Brook Green and has long been a feature of the area. You could have a tapas meal here any time within our price limit, but the top bargain is the 2-course lunch for £7.20, including tea or coffee. You might have butternut squash and sage pie, with crema catalana to finish. There's a good, short, mostly Spanish wine list kicking off at £12.80 a bottle. / www.losmolinosuk.com; closed Sat L & Sun.

Lovage SE1 £14* ★★

13-15 Elizabeth St   7403 8886   9–4D

The South Bank restaurants which benefit from views of Tower Bridge often seem to charge excessively for the privilege. All the more reason to invest five minutes in a walk away from the riverbank to this new Indian. The set lunch – £7.95 for two courses – offers value as good as you'll find anywhere in town. With a pint of lager around the £3 mark, and main menu dishes including the likes of lamb biryani (£10.50), however, you can also – with care – dine here within our budget.

Lowiczanka
Polish Social & Cultural Assoc'n W6 £20

238-246 King St   8741 3225   7–2B

Way before everyone in London seemed to be eastern European, Hammersmith was a centre for ex-pat Poles, as evidenced by this large (rather Soviet-looking) concrete cultural centre. There is a first-floor restaurant with a modern dining room where you can have the lunch special for £9.50 on weekdays and £10.50 on Sunday. Otherwise the mains are from £7.50-£15. House wine is £11.50 a bottle, or try Polish beer for £3. (Another option worth knowing about is the Café Maya at the side of the building, offering snacks and cakes that are well within budget at any time). / 11 pm, Fri 12 pm, Sat 1 am.

Lucky Seven W2 £17 A★

127 Westbourne Park Rd 7727 6771 6–1B

You may have to share your booth with strangers (probably local 'trustafarians'), if you visit Tom (son of Sir Terrence) Conran's tiny Notting Hill diner, whose funky décor is a retro homage to '50s Americana. This is one of London's top destinations for a burger (around £6.50), washed down with an imported beer (£3.50) or one of the excellent shakes (£3.95). / www.tomconranrestaurants.com; 11 pm; no Amex; no booking.

Ma Cuisine £20* ★★

7 White Hart Ln, SW13 8878 4092 10–1A
6 Whitton Rd, TW1 8607 9849 1–4A
9 Station Approach, TW9 8332 1923 1–3A

For stereotypical 'French bistro' looks, it's difficult to beat the branches of John McClement's straightforward Gallic chain. In the evenings, prices are rather outside our limit, but for a weekday lunch you can have two courses – perhaps mushroom risotto followed by salmon – for £13.95 (or £16.50 if you throw in crêpes Suzette to finish). House wine is a modest £12.50 a bottle. / 10 pm, Fri & Sat 10.30 pm; TW1 closed Sun & Mon; no Amex.

Ma Goa SW15 £17* ★

244 Upper Richmond Rd 8780 1767 10–2B

This homely, family-run Goan venture has long been one of Putney's more exciting culinary destinations as well as one of its most charming. A la carte it tests our budget, but that's certainly not the case at lunch (except Sundays) and early evenings, when there's a 2-course menu for £10 – you might have lamb kebab with ginger, then chicken in a saffron, garlic & yoghurt sauce. Drink Kingfisher for £3.25 a pint. / www.ma-goa.com; 11 pm, Sun 10 pm; closed Mon, Tue–Sat D only, Sun open L & D.

Made in Italy SW3 £22

249 King's Rd 7352 1880 5–3C

A Chelsea bistro whose long-standing reputation for decent pizza and pasta dishes (around £9.50) has made it quite an institution. There are good starters too (£4.75-£7.50). The setting can get rather noisy and crowded, though, and service can leave something to be desired. Wines are from £13.95 a bottle. / www.madeinitalyrestaurant.co.uk; 11.30 pm, Sun 10.30 pm; closed weekday L; no Amex.

Madhu's UB1 £19 ★★

39 South Rd 8574 1897 1–3A

If you're going to venture to Southall to see if the local curries are as good as everyone says, this long-established fixture on the high street is one of the safest bets. The décor is smart (especially by the standards of the area), service is very friendly, and the food (which has some Kenyan influences) is the real McCoy, with few dishes exceeding a tenner. Wines are from just £9 a bottle. / www.madhusonline.com; 11.30 pm; closed Tue, Sat L & Sun L.

Magic Wok W2 £19 ★

100 Queensway 7792 9767 6–2C

Many people don't know that Bayswater is quite a destination for those in search of quality Chinese fare. This place isn't one of the 'big' names, but it's much more welcoming than some of its better-known competitors, and it does offer good food at reasonable prices – 3-course set menus from £12.50, and wines from £10.50 a bottle. / 11 pm.

Maison Bertaux W1 £ 9 A★
28 Greek St   7437 6007   4–2A
Soho's oldest pâtisserie (est. 1871) is undoubtedly very rickety,
but that only adds to its quaint and timeless appeal. It's a delightful
place to breakfast on coffee (from £2.40) and croissants (an almond
one is £3.90), or to while away the afternoon scoffing mouth-watering
cream cakes (around £3 a go). / 11 pm, Sun 7 pm; no credit cards;
no booking.

Malabar W8 £19 A★
27 Uxbridge St   7727 8800   6–2B
A long-established curry house, just off Notting Hill Gate, whose
civilised style and skillful cooking have long made it many people's
favourite in a pricey part of town. Top value is the Sunday buffet
lunch (£9.90), but even à la carte you can dine here fairly easily
within our price limit – most curries are under £8 (more for duck
or seafood), veggie side dishes are £4.50, and rice and naans are
around £2.50. Wine from £14 a bottle. / www.malabar-restaurant.co.uk;
11.30 pm.

Malabar Junction WC1 £22 A★
107 Gt Russell St   7580 5230   2–1C
The bland façade of this smart Bloomsbury Indian belies the
civilisation offered by its rear conservatory, and gives few clues about
the interesting Keralan cuisine on offer within. Helpful staff encourage
experimentation, and there's ample choice for vegetarians (try the
vegetable malabar for £6) and lots of fish (such as kerala fish curry
for £9.75). You can drink wine (from £10 a bottle), but most people
opt for a bottle of Cobra (£4.75). / www.malabarjunction.com; 11 pm.

Mandalay W2 £13 ★★
444 Edgware Rd   7258 3696   8–4A
A friendly and perennially crowded shop-conversion, near Lord's,
which is well worth discovering for its fascinating Burmese dishes
(which mix influences Indian and Oriental) at very modest cost – top-
end dishes like spiced rice and king prawns weigh in at just £7.90,
and house wine is a modest £8.90 a bottle. / www.mandalayway.com;
11 pm; closed Sun.

Mandarin Kitchen W2 £18* ★★
14-16 Queensway   7727 9012   6–2C
Bargain-hunters might be tempted to plump for the 2-course set
menu (£10.90) at this basic but famous Bayswater Chinese, but sadly
that doesn't usually include the seafood dishes which are the whole
point of the place – scallops (£2 each) and oysters with ginger
& spring onions (£6.90) are closer to the mark. Even better, share
a lobster (around £28) – the crustacean of which they claim to sell
more than anywhere else in the UK! – between two or three people.
The house wine is £13.50 a bottle. / 11.30 pm.

Mangal Ocakbasi E8 £14 ★★
10 Arcola St   7275 8981   1–1C
This no-menu Dalston café offers some of the best cheap eats
in town – choose your hearty kebab from the array in the glass-
fronted chill counter. Dishes come served with rice, and you can also
ask the waiter for salad and for the starters that are 'on' that day. All
in all, even allowing for some BYO wine (no corkage, or buy some in-
house at £10 a bottle), you're unlikely to spend much more than half
our budget here. / www.mangal1.com; midnight; no credit cards.

Mango & Silk SW14 £21 ★★

199 Upper Richmond Rd   8876 6220   1–4A
Udit Sarkhel is a chef with a devoted following, and his smart new Indian restaurant has been an immediate hit, down Sheen way. With many main dishes for well under a tenner, and wines kicking off at £11.50 a bottle, you can have quite a feast here too, and still remain well within our budget. / www.mangoandsilk.co.uk/; 10 pm, Fri & Sat 10.30 pm; closed weekday L.

Mango Tree SE1 £19 ★

5-6 Cromwell Buildings, Red Cross Way   7407 0333   9–4C
Very handy for Borough Market, a straight-down-the-line contemporary Indian, offering good standard dishes at reasonable prices. Starters are often around the £3 mark, with many main courses around £7.50. Relatively speaking, wines – from £14.50 a bottle – seem rather pricey. / www.justmangotree.co.uk; 11 pm.

Marine Ices NW3 £17

8 Haverstock Hill   7482 9003   8–2B
The Italian cooking at this long-in-the-tooth Chalk Farm institution – which is strongest in pizza and pasta dishes (around £7 to £8) – may not be art, but it isn't terribly pricey either. What's more – as any north London kid will tell you – the real point of a visit is the mouth-watering array of sorbets and ices (whose quality is such that in days gone by they also supplied the Savoy). Single scoops of sorbet are just £1.90. Grown-up children can drink wine at £13.50 per bottle. / www.marineices.co.uk; 11 pm; closed Mon; no Amex.

Market NW1 £18* ★

43 Parkway   7267 9700   8–3B
Sadly, although it's been widely billed as a budget English bistro, you can't comfortably eat at this Camden Town newcomer within our price range à la carte. If you find yourself in this part of town, though, it's well worth checking out the 2-course set lunch, when £10 will buy you the likes of Jerusalem artichoke, spinach & Pecorino tart, followed by smoked haddock and pea risotto. House wine is £14 a bottle. / 10.30 pm; closed Sun D.

Masala Zone £17

9 Marshall St, W1   7287 9966   3–2D
147 Earl's Court Rd, SW5   7373 0220   5–2A
71-75 Bishop's Bridge Rd, W2   6–1C
80 Upper St, N1   7359 3399   8–3D
These bustling canteens are no longer as cutting-edge as once they were, and their quality has drifted a little over the years as well. For a speedy bite that's full of taste and easy on the wallet, though, they are still a dependable option, especially if you go for a thali (£7.80-£10.70). The short wine list is priced from £11.75 a bottle, or go for a bottle of Cobra at £3.25. / www.realindianfood.com; 11 pm; no Amex; no booking unless over 10.

Masters Super Fish SE1 £11 ★

191 Waterloo Rd   7928 6924   9–4A
Given its mad popularity with cabbies, you'll probably have to queue at this fun chippy Mecca just south of the Old Vic. It's worth it though for piping hot and enormous portions at great value prices: cod 'n' chips with a soft drink thrown in will set you back all of £7. It's also licensed, with house wine at £10.50 a bottle.

Mediterraneo W11   £23*   A★
37 Kensington Park Rd   7792 3131   6–1A
This bustling Italian in Notting Hill is always packed with a glamorous local crowd, and – despite its deceptive, mock-rustic looks – a meal here can be relatively pricey. Top time to visit, then, is weekday lunch, when they do a 2-course set meal for £13.50. A typical choice would be minestrone, followed by spaghetti with roasted tomatoes, parmesan & rocket. House wine is £15.70 a bottle.
/ www.mediterraneo-restaurant.co.uk; 11.30 pm; booking: max 10.

Mela   £17*   ★
152-156 Shaftesbury Ave, WC2   7836 8635   4–2B
136-140 Herne Hill, SE24   7738 5500   10–2D
Indian 'country-style cooking' has made quite a name for this busy restaurant near Cambridge Circus (which also now has a cousin in Herne Hill). It's not quite the budget 'destination' it once was, but it remains of some note for its pre-theatre menu (5pm-7pm, and after 10.30pm), which offers three courses for just £10.95. House wine is £14 a bottle.

Mem & Laz N1   £18   ★
8 Theberton St   7704 9089   8–3D
It's hard to categorise the huge menu at this lively spot, off Islington's main drag – it includes dishes such as bangers 'n' mash, but these are outnumbered by Mediterranean and Turkish options. Nothing's very pricey, though, especially if you go for the 'lunch opportunity' which offers two courses (with lots of choice) for £6.95 (three courses, £8.95). House wine is £11.95 a bottle, or drink Peroni at £2.25 a go. / www.memlaz.com; 11.30 pm, Fri & Sat midnight.

Memories of India SW7   £19
18 Gloucester Rd   7581 3734   5–1B
Unassuming but above-average, this classic Indian is worth knowing about in pricey South Kensington. With curries from about £7 and house wine at £12.50 a bottle, you can eat here comfortably within our budget at any time. / 11.30 pm.

Memsaheb on Thames E14   £18   ★
65/67 Amsterdam Rd   7538 3008   11–2D
Hidden away on the Isle of Dogs, this popular local Indian even boasts a river-view location! There's no obvious view-premium in the prices, though – main courses are largely in the £3-£5 bracket, with main courses often around the £7 mark. House wine weighs in at a bargain £9.95 a bottle. / www.memsaheb.uk.com; 11.30 pm; closed Sat L.

Le Mercury N1   £15   A
140a Upper St   7354 4088   8–2D
This archetypal budget bistro has been a feature of Islington's main drag since the early '80s and has a classic, cramped, candle-lit interior. The Gallic scoff isn't art but is extremely good value, with all starters at £3.95 (like gnocchi truffé), all main courses £6.95 (eg confit of duck leg), and puds £2.95 (such as chocolate and pecan tart). House wine is £10.45 a bottle. / www.lemercury.co.uk; 1 am.

Meson don Felipe SE1   £18   A

53 The Cut   7928 3237   9–4A

This packed stalwart tapas bar, near the Old Vic, has long been one of the capital's top cheap eats, thanks to its wonderful atmosphere, great wines (starting at £11.95 a bottle) and dependable tapas (£1.95-£5.95). Feedback in recent times has been a little less consistent than usual, but we're still hoping that's been just a blip. / 11 pm; closed Sun; no Amex; no booking after 8 pm.

Mestizo NW1   £19*   ★

103 Hampstead Rd   7387 4064   8–4C

This understated hang-out near Warren Street tube is well worth discovering, for cooking that's much more authentic than your typical Tex/Mex (and its well-stocked bar too). To stay within budget, you'll need to steer clear of main dishes, and keep to the more tapas-y menu of antojitos (lit: little whims) and tacos, all of which are in the £4-£11 price range. Or go for the £12 'taco tray'. House wine is £12.50 a bottle. / www.mestizomx.com; 11.30 pm.

Mildred's W1   £20

45 Lexington St   7494 1634   3–2D

This Soho stalwart has long been one of central London's few veggies of note, and it occupies atmospheric premises in a nicely hidden-away but central location. Main dishes are generally around £8 – this sum, for example, would buy you orange & chickpea tagine with fennel cous cous, apricot yoghurt and flat bread. Wine from £3.60 a glass. / www.mildreds.co.uk; 11 pm; closed Sun; only Maestro; no booking.

Min Jiang
The Royal Garden Hotel W8   £24*   A★★

2-24 Kensington High St   7361 1988   5–1B

One of the most implausible cheap eats in London, this grand 10th floor Oriental – whose views, over Kensington Gardens, are at their best by day – offers excellent lunchtime dim sum (around £4 a plate). If you're looking for a festive lunch that won't break the bank, this is one of our top recommendations in town – a couple could quaff a whole bottle of vin de pays (£21) plus half a dozen plates of dim sum, and still stay within our budget. / www.minjiang.co.uk.

Mirch Masala   £14   ★★

171-173 The Broadway, UB1   8867 9222   1–3A
3 Hammersmith Rd, W14   6702 4555   7–1D
1416 London Rd, SW16   8679 1828   10–2C
213 Upper Tooting Rd, SW17   8767 8638   10–2D
111 Commercial Rd, E1   7247 9992   9–2D

For dazzling Indian food at rock-bottom prices, it's hard to better these Formica-tabled but welcoming canteens (originally in Norbury, now also in Tooting, Southall and the East End). For the best value, get there noon-4pm for the buffet (£6.99), which offers three starters and five main courses, as well as rice and naan bread. BYO – no corkage. / www.mirchmasalarestaurant.co.uk; midnight.

Misato W1   £12   ★

11 Wardour St   7734 0808   4–3A

It certainly ain't anything to look at, but this Soho spot is the place to seek out if you're looking for Japanese food at rock-bottom prices. For top value, opt for the bento boxes (from about £8), washed down with sake at £3 a time. / 10.30 pm; no credit cards.

Mitsukoshi SW1 £20* ★

Dorland Hs, 14-20 Lower Regent St 7930 0317 3–3D

Only a top Japanese restaurant would occupy a drab basement under a West End department store, and in the evenings you could easily spend £100 a head here. Not appealing? Go for lunch then, and look out for the set deals, starting at £12 – for that sum, you might have sashimi, rice, miso soup, pickles and fruit. To save money stick to the oolong tea (£2.50) – otherwise go for the hot sake at £4.50 a glass. / www.mitsukoshi-restaurant.co.uk; 10 pm.

Mohsen W14 £18 ★★

152 Warwick Rd 7602 9888 7–1D

It doesn't have much of a view – except of the Olympia Homebase – but this no-nonsense canteen-like spot still packs in a wide-ranging crowd, thanks to its generous portions of quality Persian grub. Starters, such as aubergine dip, are around the £3 mark, and main courses, principally lamb kebabs, are around £12. BYO – no corkage. / midnight; no credit cards.

Mon Plaisir WC2 £15* Ⓐ★

19-21 Monmouth St 7836 7243 4–2B

This old-fashioned Gallic bistro has been going since the war and over the decades, it has expanded into a rambling warren of dining rooms. Its performance has been variable in recent years, but the pre-/post-theatre menu – £13.50 for two courses and coffee – remains one of the longest running hits in the West End. You might have foie gras & Armagnac terrine, followed by a shoulder of lamb confit. For £2 more finish off with a plate of brie. Incredibly the deal also includes a glass of vino, but further supplies can be ordered at £13.50 a bottle and upwards. / www.monplaisir.co.uk; 11.15 pm; closed Sat L & Sun.

Mona Lisa SW10 £14 ★

417 King's Rd 7376 5447 5–3B

Toffs rub shoulders with tradesmen at this Italian greasy spoon near Chelsea's World's End – a place which is typically packed to the rafters. The attraction is dependable, if basic, scoff at rock-bottom prices. In the evenings, a spinach, avocado, bacon & mushroom salad will set you back £3.50, and chicken Milanese just £6.50. The house vino is £2.50 a glass. / 11 pm; closed Sun D; no Amex.

Monmouth Coffee Company £5 Ⓐ★★

27 Monmouth St, WC2 7379 3516 4–2B
2 Park St, SE1 7645 3585 9–4C

London's number one cult coffee destination (from £2 a cup), this Borough bar does not rely for its popularity only on its proximity to London's trendiest food market. Weekend breakfasts, with good pastries on offer for a couple of pounds, are especially popular. / www.monmouthcoffee.co.uk; L & afternoon tea only; closed Sun; no Amex; no booking.

Moro EC1 £18* Ⓐ★★

34-36 Exmouth Mkt 7833 8336 9–1A

This incredible Moorish restaurant in Clerkenwell is that rarest of beasts – a continuing fashionable success. No surprise, then, that it is way outside our budget à la carte. The bar, however, offers affordable tapas dishes – a selection might include baba ganoush (£4), grilled chorizo (£4.50) and habas fritas (£3.50) – all washed down with house wine at £13 a bottle. / www.moro.co.uk; 10.30 pm; closed Sun.

sign up for the survey at hardens.com

Moti Mahal WC2   £20*   A★

45 Gt Queen St   7240 9329   4–2D

*This quality Covent Garden Indian has big plans to become
a nationwide chain (having recently raised £25m!). As house wine
at £20 a bottle suggests, it's a pretty swanky joint, and you might well
prefer to drink Kingfisher at £4 per bottle. They do have a very good
lunch deal, though, which provides two courses for a tenner –
perhaps lamb kebab with baby leaf salad, followed by chicken tikka.
/ www.motimahal-uk.com; 11.30 pm; closed Sun.*

Mr Kong WC2   £18   ★

21 Lisle St   7437 7341   4–3A

*A recent refurbishment of this Chinatown veteran was a cause
of some concern for its regulars. Fortunately they needn't have
worried – the food's just as good as ever, and the once-grungy interior
is looking rather better. A long Cantonese menu is offered, with main
dishes typically costing £7-£9, and house wine just £9.50 a bottle.
/ www.mrkongrestaurant.com; 2.45 am, Sun 1.45 am.*

Namo E9   £19   A★

178 Victoria Park Rd   8533 0639   1–2D

*Near Victoria Park, this friendly Vietnamese outfit is a pleasant all-
rounder presided over by friendly owner Lynne and offers good food
at reasonable prices. Starters might be the likes of fishcakes (£5.50),
perhaps followed by a main course chicken curry with coconut
(£7.20), washed down with house wine at £12 a bottle.
/ www.namo.co.uk; 11 pm; closed Mon, Tue L, Wed L & Thu L; no Amex.*

Nanglo SW12   £13   A★

88 Balham High Rd   8673 4160   10–2C

*The sort of good, budget all-rounder we'd all like to have on our
doorsteps, this recently refurbished Balham 'Indian' even boasts
something of a speciality – it's actually Nepalese. Vegetable samosas
will set you back all of £2.95, and a main dish of lamb with capsicum
is £7.50. Tiger beer is £2.50 for a 330ml bottle. / 11.30 pm; D only.*

Napket   £12   A

5 Vigo St, W1   7734 4387   3–3D
6 Brook St, W1   7495 5862   3–2B
342 King's Rd, SW3   7352 9832   5–3C

*Given that it trades under the cringe-inducing banner of "snob food",
this opulently furnished chain of sandwich (and so on) shops is in fact
a pretty good all-rounder, if not exactly a bargain destination.
A parma ham ciabatta, for example, will set you back £4.83, and a
tiramisu is £2.88. To drink? – perhaps a fresh fruit juice (from £2.95).*

Natural Burger Co & Grill NW8   £10   ★

12 Blenheim Terrace   7372 9065   8–3A

*It may not be a great atmosphere destination, but this St John's Wood
parlour has made quite a name for its huge, fresh burgers
(from £5.85), which make it well worth seeking out in its own right.
There is a school of thought that this is a place best taken away from,
but – if you're lingering – you can wash your meal down with
a milkshake (£2.70). / 11 pm; no Amex.*

Nautilus NW6　　　　　　　　**£13**　　★

27-29 Fortune Green Rd　7435 2532　1–1B

This veteran chippy in West Hampstead may never have been what you'd call a stylish destination, but that's hardly the point – it's the friendly service and fabulous kosher fish 'n' chips, using matzo-meal batter and offering fourteen types of fish, that are the attractions here. Basic fish 'n' chips will set you back £7, and a bottle of house wine is £9.50. / 10 pm; closed Sun; no Amex.

Navarro's W1　　　　　　　　**£22**　　★

67 Charlotte St　7637 7713　2–1C

This Fitzrovia tapas bar of long standing is neither literally nor metaphorically a bargain-basement destination. It does, however, offer an elegant West End setting in which to share some traditional tapas (generally £5 and up) and a bottle of the house vino (£14.50). / www.navarros.co.uk; 10 pm; closed Sat L & Sun.

Nazmins Balti House SW18　　**£16**　　★

398 Garratt Ln　8944 1463　10–2B

Your classic cheap 'n' cheerful Indian spot, this Earlsfield veteran offers standard fare of good quality, and at very reasonable prices. A king prawn Madras, for example, is £7.50, a naan £2.50, and house wine £12.95 a bottle. / www.nazmins.com; midnight.

New Mayflower W1　　　　　　**£18**　　★

68-70 Shaftesbury Ave　7734 9207　4–3A

Don't be put off by the 'ordinary' appearance of this authentic Chinatown spot, which is not only one of the more interesting in the area foodwise, but also one of the best places to eat in London in the early hours of morning. For the best chow, avoid the set menus, and try the more unusual dishes – the staff can be brusque, but don't be afraid to ask for advice. Most main dishes are about £7, and the house wine is £11 a bottle. / 4 am; D only; no Amex.

New Tayyabs E1　　　　　　　**£14**　　★★

83 Fieldgate St　7247 9543　9–2D

Heaving from early evening onwards (book, or risk a mad queue), this East End Pakistani packs 'em in for its stupendous dishes – in particular, brilliant curries and lamb chops. You can spend up to £12 on a dish, though most are much less, and bills are kept in check by the BYO policy. / www.tayyabs.co.uk; 11.30 pm.

New World W1　　　　　　　　**£17**

1 Gerrard Pl　7734 0396　4–3A

Lunchtime dim sum (from £2.40 per dish) – served from trolleys – is the culinary highlight at this large and chaotic Chinatown landmark. Its gaudy red and gold façade may appear to more striking effect in the evening, but dinner is a less exciting affair (even though the long menu offers ample choice within our budget). House wine is £13 a bottle. / 11.45 pm; no booking, Sun L.

Noor Jahan　　　　　　　　　**£21**　　★

2a Bina Gdns, SW5　7373 6522　5–2B

26 Sussex Pl, W2　7402 2332　6–1D

In the heart of fashionable South Kensington, and more recently in Bayswater too, these ordinary-looking curry houses are always buzzing, thanks to their reputation for offering classic dishes at reasonable prices. Chicken tikka masala is £9.10, for example, and house wine comes in at £13.50 a bottle. / 11.30 pm.

Nordic Bakery W1 £12 Ⓐ
14 Golden Sq   3230 1077   3–2D
London's semi-official gathering point for homesick Finns,
this impressive and gloomy – but elegant and spacious – modern café
makes a restful light-bite destination for those of any nationality.
Wash down your cinnamon buns (£2) and smoked salmon
sandwiches on rye (£4) with good Scandie-style coffee (£2).
/ www.nordicbakery.com; 10 pm, Sat 7 pm; closed Sat D & Sun; no booking.

The Norfolk Arms WC1 £18 Ⓐ
28 Leigh St   7388 3937   8–4C
It may not be quite clear whether this Bloomsbury spot is a gastropub
or a tapas bar, but any problems about classification have done
nothing to stop it from becoming very popular. This presumably has
something to do with the fact that it offers a good range of tasty
dishes, mainly for around the £3.50 mark. Wines kick off at £3.20
a glass. / www.norfolkarms.co.uk; 10.15 pm.

The Normanby SW15 £23 Ⓐ★
231 Putney Bridge Rd   8874 1555   10–2B
An instant hit, down Putney way, this smart new gastroboozer offers
a wide-ranging and attractively priced menu. Top-price main courses
(such as sirloin steak) weigh in around the £12 mark, and there's
plenty of choice for under a tenner – moules/frites for £7.50,
for example – so you can always be confident of eating here within
our budget. Wines by the small (125ml) glass kick off at just £2.50
a time too, so you can infuse your dining experience with a bit
of vinous variety. / www.thenormanby.co.uk; 10 pm.

North China W3 £21 ★
305 Uxbridge Rd   8992 9183   7–1A
All the more welcome in its unlikely Acton location, this is a good-all-
round Chinese restaurant, offering high-quality food at reasonable
prices – there's quite a generous 3-course menu (£14.50),
for example. Wines kick off at £3.45 a glass. / www.northchina.co.uk;
11 pm.

North Sea Fish WC1 £17 ★
7-8 Leigh St   7387 5892   8–4C
This faded-looking chippy may be located in deepest Bloomsbury,
but its dining room is not unlike a seaside tea room. It's a more than
usually comfortable institution of its type, and the fish 'n' chips (£10-
£12) are excellent. The house wine is £11.95 a bottle. Note that
early evenings are especially busy, so it's worth booking ahead.
/ 10.30 pm; closed Sun.

Nyonya W11 £18
2a Kensington Park Rd   7243 1800   6–2B
Nyonya cuisine combines Malay and Chinese traditions which is not
that common in London's Malaysian restaurants. This simple canteen
– on a corner off Notting Hill Gate – is a good-value pit stop and
makes a good place to give it a try. A selection of its stir-fries, curries
and 'Hawker favourites' would slip under our price limit at any time,
and there's also a 2-course lunch deal for £9.50. House wine
is £14.50 a bottle. / www.nyonya.co.uk; 10.30 pm.

O'Zon TW1 £24
33-35 London Rd   8891 3611   1–4A
This large pan-Oriental café in downtown Twickenham tests the price
limit we've set for this guide. Its generous, all-you-can-eat offer
(£15.95), however, is a good deal, offering a diverse range of dishes,
carefully prepared. House wine is £11 a bottle. / 11 pm.

(Ognisko Polskie)
The Polish Club SW7 £ 18* Ⓐ
55 Prince's Gate, Exhibition Rd   7589 4635   5–1C
With its time warp ambience, this dining room of a South Kensington émigrés' club can make a fun (and romantic) 'find' for first-timers, especially in summer when you can eat on the secluded back terrace. The grandeur of the setting may help you overlook the stolidity of the fodder – for £12, you might have pea soup, beef goulash and strawberries with whipped cream to finish. House wine is £12.90 a bottle. / www.ognisko.com; 11 pm.

Okawari W5 £ 17 ★
13 Bond St   8566 0466   1–3A
Ealing is short on interesting places to eat, making it all the more worth knowing about this simple, cheery Japanese café right in the centre, where much of the seating is 'tatami'-style (at sunken tables). A la carte dishes like chicken katsu curry are about £8, but for a couple of pounds more you can choose from an array of bento box meals. Drink Asahi beer for £2.80 a bottle. / www.okawari.co.uk; 11 pm, Fri & Sat 11.30 pm.

Old Parr's Head W14 £ 16
120 Blythe Rd   7371 4561   7–1C
In the backstreets behind Olympia, this traditional-style pub is worth discovering for its tasty, super-cheap Thai scoff, which is served in the crowded bar, or in summer in the pleasant rear courtyard. A typical meal would be mixed starters (£6.50) followed by chicken green curry (£6), washed down with house wine at £13.50 a bottle. / 10 pm, Sat & Sun 10.30 pm; no Amex.

Oliveto SW1 £ 25* ★
49 Elizabeth St   7730 0074   2–4A
Steer clear of the main dishes and you can (just about) squeak under our price limit at this fashionably stark Belgravia Italian. It serves some of the best thin-crust pizzas in town, with a good selection from £9-£11. Go easy on the vino at £4 a glass, and you can still round off with a tiramisu at £6.50. / www.olivorestaurants.com; 11 pm; booking: max 7 at D.

Olley's SE24 £ 18 ★
65-67 Norwood Rd   8671 8259   10–2D
All the more with knowing about in a thin area, this attractive Brockwell Park bistro is touted in some quarters as the best place in south London for fish. There's a huge range on offer, mainly in the £9-£15 range, and you can opt for grilled or steamed if you prefer. With chips at £3, and wines starting off at £14 a bottle, this is clearly no super-bargain destination, but the quality makes it worthwhile. Arrive before 7pm and fish, chips and mushy peas are just £7. / www.olleys.info; 10.30 pm; closed Mon.

Olympus Fish N3 £ 17 ★
140-142 Ballards Ln   8371 8666   1–1B
An unpretentious Finchley bistro, of note for its good-quality standard fish 'n' chips (£9.75), as well as a range of other seafood delights. You might kick off your meal, for example, with a plate of grilled calamari (£3.90). The house wine is £10.90 a bottle. / olympusfishrestaurant.co.uk; 11 pm; closed Mon.

Original Tajines W1   £18*

7a Dorset St   7935 1545   2–1A

*This cosy Marylebone café specialises in warming North African
dishes, particularly the eponymous stews. You could squeeze a meal
here within our budget at any time, but the best bargain is at lunch,
when you might have soup and a tagine for £11.50. A bottle of house
wine is £12.95. / 11 pm; closed Sat L & Sun; no Amex.*

Osteria Basilico W11   £25*   A★

29 Kensington Park Rd   7727 9957   6–1A

*Since the demise of the seminal Notting Hill restaurant '192',
this rustic Italian can claim to be the area's 'original' trendy
destination, and it remains hugely popular. There may be nothing
at all remarkable about the culinary formula – perhaps tortelloni
(£10.50), followed by tiramisu (£5), with a glass of vino for £4.60 –
but you'll still need to arrive early to have any hope of a table.
NB Stray from the pizza and pasta options and you could spend well
over our price limit here. / www.osteriabasilico.co.uk; 11.30 pm,
Sun 10.30 pm; no booking, Sat L.*

The Paddyfield SW12   £17   ★★

Bedford Hill   8772 1145   10–2C

*There's not much decoration to speak of at this long-established
Balham Oriental. Not that this fact puts off its loyal regulars, drawn
by its friendly style and excellent inexpensive Thai food
(with most main dishes ranging from £5.50-£7.90). The value
equation is boosted even more by the fact that it's unlicensed so that
you can BYO (£1 corkage). / 10.30 pm, Sat & Sun 11 pm; D only; no credit
cards.*

Il Pagliaccio SW6   £21   A

182-184 Wandsworth Bridge Rd   7371 5253   10–1B

*A mad crew of long-serving staff fuel the fun at this basic Italian
in the depths of Fulham, which majors in raucous evenings,
and chaotic kids' lunches at the weekends. Most pizza and pasta
dishes are under £8, and the house wine is £10.50 a bottle.
/ www.paggs.co.uk; midnight; no Amex.*

Le Pain Quotidien   £18

18 Great Marlborough St, W1   7486 6154   3–2C
72-75 Marylebone High St, W1   7486 6154   2–1A
174 High Holborn, WC1   7486 6154   4–1C
201-203A Kings Rd, SW3   7486 6154   5–3C
15-17 Exhibition Rd, SW7   7486 6154   5–2C
9 Young St, W8   7486 6154   5–1A
St Pancras, NW1   7486 6154   8–3C
Royal Festival Hall, SE1   7486 6154   2–3D

*Large communal tables set the convivial tone at these rustically-styled
café-bakeries, part of a Belgian-based international franchise. They
are particularly handy for a pain chocolat (£2) and a pot of coffee
(£2.20). For later in the day, there are savoury dishes such as pâté
with cornichons (£5.50) or a tuna salad (£7.95), with perhaps
a basket of breads to share (£5.20). House wine is £15 a bottle.
/ www.painquotidien.com; W1 9 pm, Sun 8 pm; SW3 10 pm, Sun 7 pm;
W8 8 pm, Sun & Mon 7 pm; SE1 11 pm, Sun 10 pm; W1F 10 pm, Sun 7 pm;
no bookings at some branches, especially at weekends.*

sign up for the survey at hardens.com   71

The Palmerston SE22 £18* ★

91 Lordship Ln 8693 1629 1–4D

This quality East Dulwich gastropub isn't that cheap an eat in the evenings. It does, however, have a very good lunch deal, offering two courses for £11 and three for £14.50. Your meal might start with roast pepper soup, followed by squid with tagliatelle and gremolata (and, if you've gone for a pud, warm orange treacle tart with cream). A bottle of house wine is £13.75. / www.thepalmerston.net; 10 pm, Sun 9.30 pm; no Amex.

Paolina Café WC1 £15 ★

181 Kings Cross Rd 7278 8176 8–3D

Bad ethnic food, as someone once – rather sweepingly – noted, begins at Calais. So if you're heading for the Eurostar, you might like to have a last fill of good budget Thai nosh at this King's Cross café. A basic set menu will set you back all of £13.50, and you even get to BYO. Corkage is 50p per person. / 10 pm; closed Sun; no credit cards.

Pappa Ciccia £17 A★

105-107 Munster Rd, SW6 7384 1884 10–1B
41 Fulham High St, SW6 7736 0900 10–1B
90 Lower Richmond Rd, SW15 8789 9040 10–1A

If you're going to check out these Fulham pizza and pasta stops, we'd especially recommend the original branch (first listed above). It offers quality Italian fare – perhaps tagliatelle carbonara (£8.50) or pizza mezzaluna (£9.50) – in cramped but characterful surroundings, and is popular for small parties. House wine is £3.50 a glass. / www.pappaciccia.com; 11 pm, Sat & Sun 11.30 pm; SW6 no credit cards.

El Parador NW1 £17

245 Eversholt St 7387 2789 8–3C

Rather unexpectedly located near Euston station, this is an authentic tapas bar, offering a good number of standard dishes, many around the £4-£5 mark, washed down with wines from £14.20 a bottle. Weekday lunchers get three tapas for the price of two. / www.elparadorlondon.com; 11 pm, Fri & Sat 11.30 pm, Sun 9.30 pm; closed Sat L & Sun L; no Amex.

The Passage Café EC1 £23 ★★

12 Jerusalem Pas 3217 0090 9–1A

Still not very well-known, this cramped and hidden-away Gallic spot in Clerkenwell was in fact one of the first of the new wave of London bistros to offer exceptional food at reasonable prices. Crêpes (around £6 for a big one) are available, but the 'real' food here is too good, and too well-priced, to ignore – you might have bavette flambée and frites (£10), for example, followed by chocolate soup with black pepper ice cream (£3.50), with wines from £16 a bottle. / www.thepassagecafe.com.

Patara £20* ★★

15 Greek St, W1 7437 1071 4–2A
3-7 Maddox St, W1 7499 6008 3–2C
181 Fulham Rd, SW3 7351 5692 5–2C
9 Beauchamp Pl, SW3 7581 8820 5–1C

This smart and serene Thai group (part of an international chain) is, sadly, generally out of our price range. Not so if you avail yourself of the set lunch menu (£12.50), which might comprise the likes of hot and sour soup followed by pad Thai, washed down with house wine at £13.95 a bottle. Or drink Thai beer at £3.75 a go. / www.pataralondon.com; 10.30 pm.

Patio W12 £22* A
5 Goldhawk Rd   8743 5194   7–1C
*With its jolly atmosphere, welcoming staff and regular live music,
this Polish spot by Shepherd's Bush Green is hard to beat for a party
night out on the cheap. Not that the Polish stodge is about to win any
awards, but the 3-course menu (always available for £16.50) offers
very fair value – you might have red borscht, followed by Golabka
(stuffed cabbage), with home made cheesecake. You also get a shot
of vodka thrown in! Celebrations may be further fuelled by house
wine at £12.50 a bottle. / 11.30 pm; closed Sat L & Sun L*

Patogh W1 £15
8 Crawford Pl   7262 4015   6–1D
*No-one chooses this basic Iranian just off the Edgware Road for
luxury. The food, though, is the genuine article, and very cheap with
mezze priced between £2-£3.50 and main courses (primarily kebabs)
from £6-£12. Though not especially a place to linger, you can BYO
(with no corkage) or drink tea at £1.50 a go.*

Paul £16 ★
115 Marylebone High St, W1   7224 5615   2–1A
29-30 Bedford St, WC2   7836 3304   4–3C
73 Gloucester Rd, SW7   7373 1232   5–2B
43 Hampstead High St, NW3   7794 8657   8–1A
147 Fleet St, EC4   7353 5874   9–2A
*France's biggest chain of 'high street' boulangerie/pâtisseries continues
to expand across the capital, which is a Good Thing – when it comes
to creating tasty bread and, in particular, tempting pastries, we Brits
still have a lot to learn. Some branches have tastefully furnished
cafés, offering the likes of quiches (£7-£8) and pastries (around £4).
/ www.paul-uk.com; 7 pm-8.30 pm; no Amex; no booking.*

Pearl Liang W2 £20* A★
8 Sheldon Sq   7289 7000   6–1C
*Like many Chinese restaurants, this opulently-decorated operation
in the new Paddington Basin development can be inexpensive
or pricey, depending on your tastes. Go carefully, though, and you can
have a memorable yet affordable meal here, in atmospheric opium-
den surroundings. Safest choice for the budget diner, however, is the
dim sum menu which – unusually – is always available. There's quite
a range, and most dishes are under £3. Wine prices start at around
£3 a glass. / www.pearlliang.co.uk; 11 pm.*

E Pellicci E2 £10 A
332 Bethnal Green Rd   7739 4873   1–2D
*The Pellici family is still in charge of this famous East End café, which
is known for its (listed) Art Deco interior. A classic cooked
breakfast (£4.80) is the classic reason to visit. At other times you
might have the likes of steak pie 'n' mash (£5.60), followed by apple
pie and cream (£2). No alcohol – a cuppa will set back 50p. / 5pm;
L only, closed Sun; no credit cards.*

Peninsular
Holiday Inn Express SE10 £21 ★

85 Bugsbys Way 8858 2028 1–3D

*It may be oddly situated in a Holiday Inn, but there is a school
of thought that this Greenwich restaurant, which looks rather like
a very large conference room, is one of the most authentic Chinese
outfits in London. Top-value choice is dim sum (most dishes from the
extensive list, £2-£3). A la carte, with many main courses around the
£8 mark, you can happily keep within our budget (or you can spend
quite a lot more). Wines start at £11.90 a bottle.*
/ www.mychinesefood.co.uk/; 11.30 pm, Sun 11 pm.

The Pepper Tree SW4 £14 Ⓐ

19 Clapham Common S'side 7622 1758 10–2D

*Few people ever have anything bad to say about this bustling Thai
canteen of long standing, by Clapham Common tube, other than that
you sometimes have to queue to get in. The simple Thai dishes –
say chicken curry laksa at £6.35 – are ultra reliable and so cheap.
House wine is £10.95 a bottle. / www.thepeppertree.co.uk; 11 pm, Sun &
Mon 10.30 pm; no Amex; no booking at D.*

Petek N4 £15 Ⓐ

96 Stroud Green Rd 7619 3933 8–1D

*Notably hospitable service adds life to this popular spot – a superior
kebab house, especially for Finsbury Park. A meal à la carte would
slip under our price limit at any time, but to be on the safe side go for
the 2-course deal for £8.45: perhaps baba ganoush then lamb shish.
House wine is £12.65 per bottle, or drink Efes lager for £3.25
a time. / 11 pm; Mon-Thu D only, Fri-Sun open L & D.*

Pham Sushi EC1 £20 ★★

159 Whitecross St 7251 6336 9–1B

*For some of the best-value Japanese food in town, head off to this
simple bar/restaurant, north of the Barbican. There's a huge menu
with a wide range of noodles, tempura and fried dishes. As its name
hints, though, it'd be a shame to skip the fantastic sushi and sashimi
here: there's a very good variety, and – if there are two or more
eating – evening set deals from £15. Drink a small bottle of sake for
£3.50. / www.phamsushi.co.uk; 10 pm; closed Sat L & Sun.*

Philpotts Mezzaluna NW2 £23* Ⓐ★★

424 Finchley Rd 7794 0455 1–1B

*David Philpott's Child's Hill fixture has long been a classic
neighbourhood spot, offering friendly service, a cosy, comfy setting
and Italian cooking that's a cut above. And good prices too! Especially
at lunch, when two courses including coffee and home-made
chocolates will set you back only £17 (three courses £20). House
wine is £14 a bottle. / www.philpotts-mezzaluna.com; 11 pm; closed Mon &
Sat L; no Amex.*

Pho £13 Ⓐ★

3 Great Titchfield St, W1 7436 0111 3–1C
Ariel Way, W12 7–1C
86 St John St, EC1 7253 7624 9–1A

*This expanding chain is now up to three outlets with the opening of a
new branch in the giant Westfield Shopping Centre. Pho –
rice noodles – are at the heart of a Vietnamese street food concept,
which works extremely well, especially when you need to fill up on
a shoestring (an 'expensive' dish like hot and spicy prawn soup
is £8.95). Slake your thirst with house wine (£13.95) or lager
(a bottle of Halida is £2.95). / www.phocafe.co.uk.*

Phoenix Bar & Grill SW15 £21* ★
162-164 Lower Richmond Rd 8780 3131 10–1A
This buzzy Putney brasserie is just the kind of neighbourhood hang-out everyone would like at the end of their road. On a budget, lunch is the time to visit when – every day except Sunday – they offer two courses for £13.50 (three for £15.50). You get a proper meal – maybe pork terrine, then chicken with fennel & roast potatoes, followed by ice cream. A bottle of house wine is £12.50.
/ www.sonnys.co.uk; 10.30 pm, 11 pm.

Phoenix Palace NW1 £23 ★
3-5 Glentworth St 7486 3515 2–1A
This restaurant near Baker Street tube always seems reassuringly popular with Orientals. In the Chinese fashion, the menu accommodates those who don't want to spend very much (with some main courses around the £8 mark), as well as those who want to spend quite a lot. At lunchtime, the budget choice is dim sum (generally £2.50-£4 each), and a limited range (around £5) is also available in the evening. Wines kick off at £14 a bottle.
/ pheonixpalace.uk.com; 11.15 pm.

Pinchito EC1 £18 ★
32 Featherstone St 7490 0121 9–1C
Not far from Old Street roundabout, this backstreet tapas – or, more specifically, 'pincho' bar – does indeed have the sort of slightly down-at-heel charm you might find at a similar establishment in San Sebastian. Standard tapas are generally around a fiver, with wines kicking off at a fairly hefty £15.75 a bottle. / www.pintxopeople.co.uk; midnight; closed Sat L & Sun.

El Pirata W1 £17
5-6 Down St 7491 3810 3–4B
The style is hardly cutting-edge, but this well-established tapas bar has long been known about for offering very keen prices, especially by Mayfair standards. A meal here wouldn't stretch our budget at any time, but the set 2-course lunch is an out-and-out bargain – you get a choice of two tapas dishes, bread and aioli, plus a small glass of wine or Mahou beer, all for £9.95. At £14.95 a bottle, however, the house vino isn't quite such a bargain. / www.elpirata.co.uk; 11.30 pm; closed Sat L & Sun.

Pizza Metro SW11 £22 Ⓐ★★
64 Battersea Rise 7228 3812 10–2C
This crowded and vivacious Battersea Italian was the first in London to import the Neapolitan tradition of selling pizza by the metre. Now 15 years old, it's still regularly packed with homesick Italians, and still serving some of the best pizza in town (as well as good pasta dishes, all around £10). The house wine is £14.95 per bottle.
/ www.pizzametropizza.co.uk; 11 pm; closed Mon, Tue-Thu D only,Fri-Sun open L & D; no Amex.

Pizza on the Park SW1 £22 Ⓐ
11 Knightsbridge 7235 5273 5–1D
They shelled out a lot on the design when they built this airy, upmarket PizzaExpress many years ago, and – after all these years – it still feels pretty stylish. For a (relatively) affordable bite near Hyde Park Corner, it has a lot going for it, and pizza and pasta dishes are around a tenner. Reflecting the area, though, the house wine is £15.25 a bottle. (The famous jazz venue in the basement is, sadly, beyond our budget.) / www.pizzaonthepark.co.uk; 11 pm, Fri & Sat midnight.

PizzaExpress £18

Branches throughout London

The grand-daddy of all London's mid-market chains, this celebrated group still reliably brings a degree of class to the budget dining experience which is difficult to match. For many families, it remains the default option for a meal out (and there's a good, if not especially generous, special menu for the little ones, £5.65). Of late, the adult menu has even seen a bit of innovation – for example, the new top-of-the-range Roman-style pizzas (such as the Salsiccia, with Italian sausage and yellow peppers, £9.25) are pretty good. House wine is £12.65 a bottle. / www.pizzaexpress.co.uk; 11.30 pm-midnight; most City branches closed all or part of weekend; no booking at most branches.

Pizzeria Oregano N1 £17 ★

19 St Albans Pl   7288 1123   8–3D

In a side street, a few yards away from the chain-extravaganza which is Islington's Upper Street, lurks an unpretentious, individually-owned pizzeria whose pizzas (£5.95-£7.95) are generally above the norm. The house wine is £12.50 a bottle. / 11.30 pm, Sun 10.30 pm; closed Mon, Tue-Fri D only, Sat & Sun open L & D; no Amex.

The Place Below EC2 £12 𝔸★

St Mary-le-Bow, Cheapside   7329 0789   9–2C

This veteran self-service veggie cafeteria in the heart of the City – occupying the atmospheric crypt under St Mary-le-Bow – is unlike anything else in the Square Mile. The daily selection is small but carefully prepared – you might have pumpkin & lentil soup (£3.20) followed by spinach, walnut & feta pie with salad (£7.75). No booze – coffee from £1.45. / www.theplacebelow.co.uk; L only, closed Sat & Sun; no Amex; need 15+ to book.

Le Pont de la Tour Bar & Grill SE1 £25* 𝔸★

36d Shad Thames   7403 8403   9–4D

It seems unlikely that this grand modern French restaurant, with magnificent views of Tower Bridge, could be a 'cheap eat' (and the deal we rate is, to be frank, just a few pence over our budget). Visit the bar for lunch, however, and you can enjoy a 2-course lunch for just £13.50 – perhaps pumpkin soup, followed by a smoked haddock quiche. Go easy on the drink – the list here is one of the capital's heavyweights, and starts at £19.50 a bottle. / www.lepontdelatour.co.uk; 11 pm, Sun 10 pm; no booking.

Popeseye £24*

108 Blythe Rd, W14   7610 4578   7–1C

277 Upper Richmond Rd, SW15   8788 7733   10–2A

On a good day, these no-frills bistros in Brook Green and Putney are among the very best places in London for a decent Scottish steak, so we think it worth listing an establishment which tests our budget – you'll need to stick to an 8oz popeseye (rump) with chips which will set you back £13.45, and a pudding £4.95. The small but expertly-sourced selection of wines kicks off at £12.50 a bottle. / www.popeseye.com; 10.30 pm; D only, closed Sun; no credit cards.

La Porchetta Pizzeria   £17
33 Boswell St, WC1   7242 2434   2–1D
141-142 Upper St, N1   7288 2488   8–2D
147 Stroud Green Rd, N4   7281 2892   8–1D
74-77 Chalk Farm Rd, NW1   7267 6822   8–2B
84-86 Rosebery Ave, EC1   7837 6060   9–1A
*As evidenced by big queues (especially at the Finsbury Park original),
sheer value has won a huge following for these jolly and brightly-lit
north London pizzerias. They really are not expensive. With starters
from £3.80, gigantic pizzas around £7 and the house wine at £11
a litre, you won't do much better than this if you're looking for a blow-
out on a budget. / varies; WC1 closed Sat L & Sun, N1 Mon-Thu closed
L, N4 closed weekday L; no Amex.*

Potemkin EC1   £17*
144 Clerkenwell Rd   7278 6661   9–1A
*The list of 108 vodkas (around £3 per shot) is undoubtedly the high
point of this Russian outfit, which is stuck out on a limb near
St Peter's Italian church in Clerkenwell. The upstairs bar offers
a range of very affordable 'zakusi' (snacks). The downstairs
restaurant can be less atmospheric, but – if you're in the area –
the 2-course weekday menu for £10 (lunch) or £15 (dinner) may
be worth seeking out. The house wine is £12.50 a bottle.
/ www.potemkin.co.uk; 10.30 pm; closed Sat L & Sun.*

Preto SW1   £21
72 Wilton Rd   7233 8668   2–4B
*Need to fill up on a budget? Look no further than this recent Pimlico
opening about 10 minutes's walk from Victoria Station. It runs an all-
you can eat Brazilian BBQ and buffet which would leave Mr Creosote
full, and whose wide spread of tasty dishes has something for
everyone. Weekday lunch is £13.95 (and just £9.95 on Monday),
with house wine at £12 a bottle. In the evening – other than
on Monday's (when the buffet £13.95) – and at weekends, it's a little
out of our price range.*

Princess Victoria W12   £18*   ★
217 Uxbridge Rd   8749 5886   7–1B
*It's always uplifting to see a fine old pub rescued from the knacker's
yard. This vast Victorian pile on the Shepherd's Bush/Acton borders
has scrubbed up magnificently, and was one of the better arrivals
of 2008. As gastropubs go, it's not especially cheap, but they do a
weekday lunch with two courses for £12.50 (three for £15). There's
an award-winning wine list starting from £14.50 a bottle, or drink
a nice pint of Peroni for £3.95. / www.princessvictoria.co.uk; 10.30 pm,
Sun 9.30 pm.*

Princi W1   £14   𝔸★
135 Wardour St   7478 8888   3–2D
*The Milanese call their star local baker, Rocco Princi, the "Armani del
pane", and when you see this extremely elegant new Soho canteen-
cum-pâtisserie, you can see why – in London, you simply won't find
anywhere for a light meal which shows off this sort of bella figura.
Cakes and desserts (around £3.50) are particularly good – ideal for
an indulgent snack, washed down with an espresso (£1.40). For
lunch, add a pasta or one of the other hot dishes of the day (up to
£6), and a glass of wine (from £4). / www.princi.it.*

Priory House W14   £22

58 Milson Rd   7371 3999   7–1C

A surprisingly cool hang out in the backstreets of Olympia, this dimly-lit bar is now of note for its tapas and its cocktails. Those on a budget, however, may prefer to drink the house wine at £5 a glass, as an accompaniment to the dependable (if fairly standard) range of tapas (£3.95-£7.95). / www.priorybars.com; 10 pm; no Amex.

(Tapa Room)
The Providores W1   £22*   A★

109 Marylebone High St   7935 6175   2–1A

This ever-popular and noisy bar/diner is on the ground floor of the Marylebone HQ of Kiwi-chef Peter Gordon, the 'Sugar Club' chef who has won fame for his East-meets-West cuisine. Its eclectic brunch – anyone for feta & edamame tortilla, with pepper salsa & yoghurt (£7.80)? – is the top draw, but at any time there's a funky selection of tapas for £2.40-£5.80, with large dishes ranging from £5-£16. The wine list here is an attraction in itself, and starts from £14.50 a bottle. / www.theprovidores.co.uk; 10.30 pm.

Pure California   £12

102 Wardour St, W1   7287 4008   3–2D
39 Beak St, W1   7287 3708   3–2D
47 Goodge St, W1   7436 3601   2–1C
113 High Holborn, WC1   7242 3533   2–1D
41-43 Ludgate Hill, EC4   7242 3533   9–2A

If you're keen on healthy living and fancy a tasty cheap snack, check out this Cal-inspired chain's nutritious range of soups, sarnies and salads (with over 60 ingredients available for combinations). These last typically cost something over a fiver, with wraps closer to £3. Unlicensed: drink smoothies or juices for a little under £3. / www.purecalifornia.co.uk; W1T 6 pm; WC1 7 pm, Fri 6 pm, Sat 5 pm; W1F 7 pm, Fri & Sat 6 pm; W1T closed Sat & Sun, WC1 & W1F closed Sun.

Putney Station SW15   £20

94-98 Upper Richmond Rd   8780 0242   10–2B

It isn't just the handy location which commends this west London bistro. It's part of John Brinkley's empire, and, to those in the know, that spells just one thing – Incredible Value Wine. Very respectable Rioja, for example, is £10 a bottle, and there are even better bargains for those prepared to spend a few pounds more. The food is a bit of a supporting attraction, but it's filling enough, and few main courses are more than a tenner. / www.brinkleys.com; 11 pm, Tues-Sat midnight.

The Quality Chop House EC1   £23   ★

94 Farringdon Rd   7837 5093   9–1A

This 'Progressive Working Class Caterer' (as it says on the window) was founded in Victorian times to help the lower orders keep the wolf from the door. The institution was lovingly restored in the '90s, but its famously bum-numbing wooden benches were left intact. Prices nowadays tend to the bourgeois, but the fare is of good quality – perhaps soup (around a fiver) followed by a dish such as corned beef hash with fried egg (a tenner), washed down with house wine at £13.50 a bottle. / www.qualitychophouse.co.uk; 11.30 pm, Sun 10.30 pm; closed Sat L.

Queen's Head W6 £16

13 Brook Grn 7603 3174 7–1C

It may not be the most 'gastro' of London destinations, but this cosy, ancient tavern on Brook Green boasts a notably vast and well-decked out garden. Ignore the more expensive options on the large menu and opt for stuff like burgers for £8.95 or fish 'n' chips for £8.25. Drink house wine at £10.95 per bottle or a pint of London Pride for £3.10. / www.thespiritgroup.com; 10 pm, Sun 9 pm; no booking.

Le Querce SE23 £23* ★

66-68 Brockley Rise 8690 3761 1–4D

In an inauspicious suburb of Lewisham, this unpretentious little restaurant is perhaps the closest thing to a proper Mamma and Pappa Italian you'll find around London. Prices have crept up a bit in recent times, but main courses are still relatively affordable (£9-£14), and you can still get very good plates of pasta from £7.50 upwards. Whatever you do, try to include a pudding (£4.50) – they're excellent. House wine is £11.50 a bottle. / 10.30 pm; closed Mon; no Amex.

Ragam W1 £15 ★

57 Cleveland St 7636 9098 2–1B

This veteran south Indian in the shadow of the Telecom Tower just goes on and on. It's certainly not the décor which keeps fans returning year-in-year-out, however. More to the point are the smiling staff, and the fabulous scoff, much of it veggie, at bargain prices. Starters are £3-£5 and main dishes £5-£8.50. House wine is a tenner a bottle. / www.ragam.co.uk; 11 pm, Fri & Sat 11.30 pm, Sun 10.30 pm.

Rani N3 £20 ★

7 Long Ln 8349 4386 1–1B

This Finchley Indian is known for its great-value vegetarian buffet (mostly featuring Gujarati dishes). At dinner it costs £13.90, but if you eat early (between 6pm-8pm) it's just £9.90 (or, for Sunday lunch, £11.90). The selection includes 4 starters, 7 curries, 3-4 desserts, rice and bread. A small bottle of Cobra is £2.70, but the best deal may be an £8 jug of lassi, which serves 4-5 people. / www.raniuk.com; 10 pm; D only, ex Sun open L & D.

Ranoush £11

22 Brompton Rd, SW1 7235 6999 5–1D
338 King's Rd, SW3 7352 0044 5–3C
43 Edgware Rd, W2 7723 5929 6–1D
86 Kensington High St, W8 7938 2234 5–1A

The original Edgware Road pit stop is still the best-known branch of the Maroush Group's chain of Lebanese café/take-aways, but all its outlets are worth knowing about. They offer genuine-tasting Middle Eastern fast food at good prices – a shawarma is £3.75, and mezze dishes like hummus £3.25. There's no alcohol – drink delicious fresh fruit juices for a couple of quid. Don't expect many pleasantries from the staff. / www.maroush.com; 1 am-3 am.

Rasa N16 £17* ★★

55 Stoke Newington Church St 7249 0344 1–1C

Few restaurants inspire their fans more than this seminal Stoke Newington Indian, whose magnificent and exotic Keralan dishes wow many a carnivore too. And it's so cheap. The 'Kerala Feast' is £16, but if you DIY, dishes are typically £3-£6. Drink Cobra for £4.25 a bottle. / www.rasarestaurants.com; 10.45 pm, Fri & Sat 11.30 pm; closed weekday L.

Rasa   £19   ★★

5 Charlotte St, W1   7637 0222   2–1C
6 Dering St, W1   7629 1346   3–2B
1 Kings Cross, WC1   7833 9787   8–3D
56 Stoke Newington Church St, N16   7249 1340   1–1C

Rasa's spin-offs have moved away from the exclusively veggie focus of the Stoke Newington original. At the Dering Street offshoot and Stoke Newington's 'Travanancore' branch, carnivores are now fully catered for. Menus differ between branches, but starters are typically below a fiver, and main dishes include much in the £7-£9 price bracket, with house wine at £11.95 a bottle. (NB We've listed Charlotte Street's 'Samudra,' a pricier seafood specialist, only for completeness.) / www.rasarestaurants.com; 10.45 pm; Dering St W1 closed Sun, N16 D only Mon-Sat, N1 L only Mon-Fri, Charlotte St W1 closed Sun L, NW1 Mon - Fri L only, Rathbone St W1 Mon - Fri L only, WC1 closed Sun.

Ratchada SE3   £20

129 Lee Rd   8318 0092   1–4D

Just a good classic local Thai restaurant, in Blackheath. If you went for the grill dishes (often around the £15 mark) you could easily bust our budget, but if you stick to the more general run of the menu – curries are generally around £7 – you'd really have to try quite hard to bust it. Especially as wines kick off at a modest £10.75 a bottle. / www.ratchada.co.uk; 11 pm; closed Sun; no Amex.

Rebato's SW8   £15   A★

169 South Lambeth Rd   7735 6388   10–1D

The undying popularity of this festive Spanish veteran is all-the-more impressive given its grungy location in a Vauxhall no-man's-land. To step into the tapas bar, complete with its unchanging crew of retainers, is like being transported to Spain, and you can enjoy some great, cheap nosh (most dishes, £2-£5). To the rear, the restaurant isn't quite such good value, but has its own tacky charm. The house wine is £12.95 a bottle. / www.rebatos.com; 10.45 pm; closed Sat L & Sun.

Red Fort W1   £21*   ★

77 Dean St   7437 2525   4–2A

This famous Soho Indian is normally way, way out of our price range, so it's all the more worth knowing about its 2-course deals at lunch (£12) or pre-theatre till 7pm (£16, including coffee). In either case you get a choice of 3 starters, then 3-4 main dishes with rice and veg'. To stick to budget, steer well clear of the vino – a bottle of house is £25! – and gently sip Kingfisher at £3.95 per 330ml bottle. / www.redfort.co.uk; 11.30 pm; closed Sat L & Sun.

The Red Pepper W9   £24   ★

8 Formosa St   7266 2708   8–4A

This Maida Vale pizzeria has long been a key neighbourhood hang-out and is typically crammed (in every sense). Stick to the range of pizzas from the wood-burning oven (£8-£12) and drink house wine at £3.75 a glass, and you should have just enough slack within our budget for a tiramisu (£5). / 11 pm, Sun 10 pm; closed weekday L; no Amex.

(Restaurant, Level 7)
Tate Modern SE1 £24 A

Bankside   7887 8888   9–3B

It's the breath-taking view of the City which justifies at least one trip to Tate Modern's stark 7th floor café – try to visit at sunset. The food – perhaps cauliflower soup (£5) followed by steamed mussels (£9.70) – is variable in quality (but prices are invariably toppish). The house wine is £14.50 a bottle. / www.tate.org.uk; 9.30 pm; Sun-Thu closed D.

Riccardo's SW3 £23 A

126 Fulham Rd   7370 6656   5–3B

If you need a place to meet up with friends in Chelsea, this buzzing Italian favourite is hard to beat. Its wide-ranging menu offers many dishes in smaller portions – soups are £5-£6, pastas range from about £7 and a pizza is £8.95. If you eat between 3.30pm-6.30pm at the weekend, you can choose from a special tapas menu with all dishes at £3.50. House wine is £13.50 a bottle. / www.riccardos.it; 11.30 pm.

El Rincón Latino SW4 £18 A

148 Clapham Manor St   7622 0599   10–2D

Inexpensive wine (£12.50 a bottle) is just one of the reasons for the success of this authentic and always-busy Clapham tapas bar. Make a meal of classic tapas, such as Spanish sausages and lamb casserole (both around a fiver). / 11.30 pm; closed Mon, Tue L, Wed L, Thu L, Fri L & Sun D.

Rock & Sole Plaice WC2 £17 ★

47 Endell St   7836 3785   4–1C

To eat well and cheaply amidst the tourist tat of Covent Garden is no mean feat, especially if you want a place for a group get-together. This venerable chippy (est. 1871, so they say) is just the job – sufficiently away from the market not to be too heaving, but close enough for convenience. A calamari starter comes in at £4, cod 'n' chips is a tenner. Drink house wine at a lowly £8 per bottle, or Budvar at £2.50 a pop. / 11 pm; no Amex.

Rocket £21* A

4-6 Lancashire Ct, W1   7629 2889   3–2B
Brewhouse Ln, SW15   8789 7875   10–2B
6 Adams Ct, EC2   7628 0808   9–2C

If you're looking for a reasonably-priced rendezvous just off Bond Street, the choice is not exactly overwhelming, so the W1 branch of this stylish small chain is particularly worth seeking out. And Putney is a favourite in summer with its riverside tables. To stay within budget, some care will be needed, but it is possible if you choose the likes of fried baby squid with rocket (£5.50), followed by a house-speciality pizza (around a tenner), washed down with house wine at £15 a bottle. / www.rocketrestaurants.co.uk; 10.45 pm; W1 closed Sun; E6 & EC2 closed Sat & Sun.

Rooburoo N1 £19

21 Chapel Mkt   7278 8100   8–3D

Oddly located in Islington's long and scruffy street market, this contemporary-style Indian has made quite a name for itself. This is a comfortable place, where you can eat within our price limit at any time, with starters and puddings around the £4 mark, and main courses roughly twice that. The house wine is £12.50 a bottle. / www.rooburoo.com; 11 pm; closed Mon L.

sign up for the survey at hardens.com 81

Rosa's E1 £19

12 Hanbury St 7247 1093 9–1D

A little way off Brick Lane, near Spitalfields Market, this simple, new Thai canteen is just the job for a flavoursome quick bite that won't break the bank, with most starters around a fiver and most main dishes a little under a tenner. Drink house wine for £12 a bottle. / www.rosaslondon.com.

Rôtisserie Jules £18

6-8 Bute St, SW7 7584 0600 5–2B

133 Notting Hill Gate, W11 7221 3331 6–2B

You can have chicken, chicken, or chicken (or leg of lamb if you call ahead) at these simple Gallic rôtisseries, worth knowing about for offering cheap, healthy fast food in pricey neighbourhoods. You can have your bird in a wrap (£4.75), burger or a breaded escalope or just as it comes – for a family, a whole chicken with two sides (say fries and 'slaw) would be £20. House wine is £13.95 a bottle. / www.rotisseriejules.com; 10.30 pm.

Royal China £24* ★

24-26 Baker St, W1 7487 4688 2–1A

805 Fulham Rd, SW6 7731 0081 10–1B

13 Queensway, W2 7221 2535 6–2C

30 Westferry Circus, E14 7719 0888 11–1B

They may be glitzy, but the branches of the Royal China chain are the 'gold standard' by which other Chinese restaurants are judged. At weekends, though, they can be frantic – especially in Bayswater – as queues for the brilliant lunchtime dim sum stretch out the door. With most dishes at £2.65-£3.50, this is a culinary adventure just about anyone can afford to try. At other times, you'll have to pick carefully to stay within budget, with main courses from £8.50 and up, and house wine from £18 a bottle. / 10.45 pm, Fri & Sat 11.15 pm; no bookings Sat & Sun L.

Running Horse W1 £22

50 Davies St 7493 1275 3–2B

Decent gastropubs are a rarity in the West End. This characterful boozer is one of the few, and – with prices no higher than out in the 'burbs – a welcome find in swanky Mayfair. A range of sarnies (such as the 'Running Horse BLT') comes in around £8, a dish like sausages 'n' mash will set you back £9.25. Drink house wine at £15 a bottle, or a nice pint of Amstel for £3.55. / www.therunninghorselondon.co.uk; 9.30 pm; closed Sun D; need 8+ to book.

The Rye SE15 £20 Ⓐ

31 Peckham Rye 7639 5397 1–4D

Down Peckham Rye way, this recently-opened gastropub, with pleasant garden, has become very popular. The food often has a bit of an Oriental twist, so your meal might be a Thai green chicken curry (£9), followed by a piece of chocolate fudge cake (£4.75), washed down with house wine at £12.50 a bottle. / 10 pm, Sun 9 pm; no Amex.

Sabor N1 £24* ★

108 Essex Rd 7226 5551 8–3D

This colourful Islington South American – an uncompromising space of railway-carriage proportions – is usually busy. A la carte you might bust our limit, but the top budget tip is the 2-course set menu at £15 (3-course at £17.50).You might have sweetcorn fritters then moqueca (a Brazilian fish stew). Drink house wine at £13.50 or grab a cocktail for about £6. / www.sabor.co.uk; 10.45 pm; closed Mon, Tue-Fri D only, Sat & Sun open L & D; no Amex.

Le Sacré-Coeur N1 £13* A

18 Theberton St   7354 2618   8–3D

A quintessentially jolly bistro, off Islington's Upper Street, where you could squeeze a meal into our price limit at just about any time. But why scrimp when you can visit on any weekday lunchtime and take advantage of the set lunch at a mere £6.95 for two courses (or £8.50 for three)? (The same deals cost a fraction more at weekends.) You might have avocado salad, followed by fish casserole, with crème caramel to finish. No need to stint on the wine – it's £12 a bottle. / www.lesacrecoeur.co.uk; 11 pm, Sat 11.30 pm.

Sagar £14 ★★

17a, Percy St, W1   7631 3319   3–2B

157 King St, W6   8741 8563   7–2C

27 York St, TW1   8744 3868   1–4A

It's hard to beat veggie south Indian dishes for out-and-out value, and nowhere is this more true than these welcoming, if unremarkable-looking, cafés. If you really want to slash prices, go with the weekday lunch for a measly £5.25, when you might have a bhaji starter, followed by a curry with rice, and payasam (a sweetened rice dish) to finish. A 660ml Kingfisher beer is £4.95, or drink house wine at £12.95 a bottle. / www.gosagar.com; Sun-Thu 10.45 pm, Fri & Sat 11.30 pm.

Saigon Saigon W6 £21

313-317 King St   8748 6887   7–2B

This Hammersmith Vietnamese offers a good all-round experience, combining atmospheric, rather romantic décor with professional service and fresh-tasting cooking at an affordable price. You can squeeze a meal in here at any time. They offer various set lunch menus ranging from £6.95-£8.95 which could include spring rolls and Vietnamese noodles. House wine is £12.50 a bottle. / www.saigon-saigon.co.uk; 11 pm, Sun 10 pm; closed Mon L; no Amex.

St Alban SW1 £25* A★

4-12 Regent St   7499 8558   3–3D

The ex-Ivy team of Christopher Corbin and Jeremy King have quite a following among London's movers and shakers, so it's no surprise that their swanky Theatreland venture – complete with offbeat '70s airport lounge décor – is generally way beyond our budget. Pre- and post-theatre (5.30pm-6.30pm, and after 10pm), however, you can avail yourself of a 2-course menu for just £15.50 – you might have cauliflower and saffron soup followed by paella with seafood, chicken and chorizo. There's a first-class wine list with over 20 choices by the glass, starting at £5. / www.stalban.net; midnight, Sun 11 pm.

St John EC1 £22* ★

26 St John St   7251 0848   9–1B

Fergus Henderson's Smithfield shrine to 'Nose to Tail Eating' is world famous for its uncompromising menu of British traditional dishes. You wouldn't expect it to be any sort of bargain, and – with wines from £18 a bottle – you would be right. Even on our budget, though, a flavour of the experience is available by eating in the adjoining bar – you might have bone marrow on toast (£6.70), followed by a rhubarb trifle (£6.60). / www.stjohnrestaurant.com; 11 pm; closed Sat L & Sun D.

St John Bread & Wine E1 £21 ★★
94-96 Commercial St 7251 0848 9–1D
This Spitalfields spin-off from the legendary Smithfields venture of the same name gives you a flavour of the original, but at lower prices. Open all day, it offers a mix of British dishes cleverly combining the traditional and the modern. In the evening there are some more expensive main courses but, for the most part, dishes like crispy pig tail, chicory & mustard or hare & black cabbage can be had for £6-£7. Either kick off with a salad (£4) or finish with blood orange meringue (£5.70). Wine isn't that cheap (starting at £17 a bottle) but the selection is outstanding. / www.stjohnbreadandwine.com; 10.30 pm; closed Sun D.

Sakonis £17 ★
129 Ealing Rd, HA0 8903 9601 1–1A
180-186 Upper Tooting Rd, SW17 8772 4774 10–2C
For a brilliant, cheap meal, it's tough to match this large Wembley canteen (which nowadays also has a Tooting spin-off). The varied, vegetarian menu – which mixes 'n' matches Indian and Chinese dishes – is daunting at first, but nothing is too pricey, and most of it is delicious. The top deal is their excellent-value buffet, offering 15-20 options at lunch (£7.99); getting on for twice that number in the evening (£10.99). Unlicensed, drink a lassi or juice for around £3.

Sakura W1 £19 ★
9 Hanover St 7629 2961 3–2C
A visit to this frenetic Japanese basement, just off Mayfair's Hanover Square, is not for the faint-hearted. First, you have to secure a table from the not-always-helpful greeting staff. And then, with little guidance, you have to negotiate the bewildering menu. But don't be discouraged! You can eat well here within our price limit at any time – most cheaply from the set lunch deals starting at £8. House wine is £15 a bottle, or you may just want to stick to the free green tea. / 10 pm.

Salade £14
52 Stratton St, W1 7499 6565 3–3C
Paddington Station, W2 7402 5616 6–1C
144-146 Fetter Ln, EC4 7242 7972 9–2A
3 Old Bailey, EC4 7248 6612 9–2A
Arguably these places are inexpensive rather than cheap, but if designer salad's your bag these shiny joints fit the bill nicely. There's a large counter where you put together your choice from a bewildering array of items and toppings, or you can go for a wrap (from £3.75) or soup (from £3). Drink 'power' juices (£2.50) or smoothies (£3.80). / www.salade.co.uk; L only, W2 7 pm, Sat & Sun 5 pm; closed Sat & Sun; no Amex.

Salt Yard W1 £22 ★★
54 Goodge St 7637 0657 2–1B
There just aren't enough places like this Fitrovia tapas bar, which has a casual and welcoming style, and offers novel and brilliantly made Spanish and Italian tapas. From the main menu, an interesting dish like partridge ravioli can be sampled for just £5.75, and there's also a 'charcuterie and bar snacks' menu majoring in top quality cured meats for £8-£9. At £15 a bottle the wine 'entry level' is high, but the Spanish/Italian list is notably carefully selected. / www.saltyard.co.uk; 11 pm; closed Sat L & Sun.

Sam's Brasserie W4 £18*
11 Barley Mow Pas   8987 0555   7–2A
Despite its chichi reputation, Chiswick's main drag has traditionally been something of a chain-hell on the restaurant front, so this large brasserie – brainchild of Sam Harrison, ex–maître d' at Rick Stein's famous Seafood Restaurant – has attracted what you might describe as the more discerning sort of local family following. Most of the time it's a bit beyond our budget, but the £12, 2-course weekday lunch – perhaps pickled mackerel & salad, followed by pesto & goat's cheese linguine – brings it within reach. The house wine is £14 a bottle.
/ www.samsbrasserie.co.uk; 10.30 pm; booking: max 12.

Santo W10 £18*   ★
299 Portobello Rd   8968 4590   6–1A
By the Bohemian (northern) section of the market, this welcoming new Mexican restaurant makes a handy stand-by for Portobello's weekend flâneurs (and a particularly good destination for families with kids too). Prices by day are very reasonable (generally well under a tenner), but the (more ambitious) evening menu falls, sadly, a little outside our price bracket. Wines start at £16 a bottle.
/ www.santovillage.com.

Sapori WC2 £20
43 Drury Ln   7836 8296   4–2D
This reasonably-priced Italian is a useful stand-by in Covent Garden, and relatively un-touristy thanks to its off-the-beaten track location (which is nonetheless convenient for the Opera House). Most pizza and pasta dishes are around the £9 mark, and the house wine is £12.90 a bottle. / 11.30 pm; no Amex.

Satay House W2 £25*   ★
13 Sale Pl   7723 6763   6–1D
For a meal full of flavour at reasonable prices, this long-established Malaysian restaurant in Bayswater, recently refurbished, still delivers the goods. The menu is wide-ranging, which is both good and bad: this is one of those places where you could spend relatively little, or quite a lot. With house wines at £4.80 a glass, this is at the very limits of what you might call a 'budget' destination.
/ www.satay-house.co.uk; 11 pm.

Satsuma W1 £17   ★
56 Wardour St   7437 8338   3–2D
This big and bright Soho refectory is like a more colourful Wagamama with a wider menu (including sushi as well as noodle dishes). Another similarity is the queues. You can eat within budget here at any time, but it's cheaper at lunch, with bento box meals from £11.60 and up. A large Kirin beer is £4.20, or a bottle of house wine will set you back £15. / www.osatsuma.com; 10.30 pm; no booking.

The Sea Cow SE22 £19
37 Lordship Ln   8693 3111   1–4D
When it first opened, this post-modern chippy looked set to storm the capital with branches opening in Clapham and Fulham. Now, only this – the East Dulwich original – remains. It's still a good formula, though, with an interesting selection of fish (served grilled or battered), plus seafood options like crab cakes and mussels, all for about £8-£9. A short wine list runs from £12 a bottle.
/ www.theseacow.co.uk; 10.30 pm, Sun 8.30 pm.

Seafresh SW1 £19
80-81 Wilton Rd 7828 0747 2–4B
Especially in still remarkably under-served Pimlico, it's well worth knowing about this long-established chippy, which was given quite a smart makeover a couple of years ago, and which has a comfortable dining room attached. Your classic cod 'n' chips will set you back £9.75, and a glass of the house wine is £3.65. / 10.30 pm; closed Sun.

Seashell NW1 £24 ★
49 Lisson Grove 7224 9000 8–4A
This famous chippy near Marylebone Station has become a firm fixture on the tourist map, despite its miserable décor. Its realisation of our national dish is very good, though at £12.95 for cod 'n' chips it ought to be. For pudding, go the whole traditional route, and have spotted dick (£3.95). House wine is £12.25 a bottle. / www.seashellrestaurant.co.uk; 10.30 pm; closed Sun D.

Shampers W1 £22* Ⓐ
4 Kingly St 7437 1692 3–2D
This '70s gem of a Soho wine bar is just five minutes' walk from Piccadilly Circus. Presided over by owner Simon, it's just the place for a buzzy lunch or relaxed evening meal, fuelled by a well-chosen wine list offering 40 options by the glass (from £3.95). The food is simple but honest – grilled aubergine salad is a typical starter at £5, a main dish might be sausages with mash & red cabbage for £9. / www.shampers.net; 11 pm; closed Sun (& Sat in Aug).

Shanghai E8 £23 Ⓐ★
41 Kingsland High St 7254 2878 1–1C
Sited in the prettily tiled premises of a once-famous pie 'n' eel shop, this friendly Dalston Chinese is a slightly unusual destination. Get a seat in the boothed front section if you can (and beware of the deafening karaoke nights). Set menus are available (three courses, £16) at any time, or go for the extensive lunchtime dim sum menu. House wine is £10.50 a bottle. / www.wengwahgroup.com; 11 pm; no Amex.

Shikara SW3 £20
87 Sloane Ave 7581 6555 5–2C
Given how chichi Brompton Cross is nowadays, this very 'plain vanilla' Indian can come as something of a surprise. For a nice hot curry, though, this is the place, with most options ranging in price between £7.95-£12.95. House wine is £11.50 a bottle. / www.shikara.co.uk; 11.30 pm.

Shilpa W6 £16 ★
206 King St 8741 3127 7–2B
This small modern Indian is indistinguishable from the many on Hammersmith's main drag. Not so the Keralan cooking, however, whose high quality at ludicrously cheap prices approaches those of its more famous siblings, Ragam and Malabar Junction. You could stuff yourself senseless and still have change from our budget here, with most main courses about £6. At lunch, the vegetarian set meal is just £3.99! Drink Cobra at £3.90 a bottle. / www.shilparestaurant.co.uk.

The Ship SW18 £22   🅐

41 Jews Row   8870 9667   10–2B

On a sunny day, over-popularity is the main problem of this Wandsworth riverside boozer, which is a top spot for a BBQ in the garden. At other times, though, it still makes a characterful destination, with dependable grub that's most economically enjoyed from the weekday lunch deals. This comprises two courses for £13.50 (three for £16). You might enjoy mackerel salad, then braised beef cheek Bourguignon with dauphinoise and – if you still have room – lemon tart. House wine is £13.50 a bottle, or drink a pint of Young's Bitter for £2.80. / www.theship.co.uk; 10 pm; no booking, Sun L.

Siam Central W1 £14

14 Charlotte St   7436 7460   2–1C

The 2-course lunch deal for £7.50 is a prime draw to this cheap 'n' cheerful Fitzrovia Thai. A typical selection would be vegetable spring rolls, then a sweet 'n' sour stir fry. House wine is £11.75 a bottle. / 11 pm.

Simpson's Tavern EC3 £18   🅐

38 1/2 Ball Ct, Cornhill   7626 9985   9–2C

This timeless chophouse, in a City back-alley, offers an experience as close as you'll find to how it must have been to eat in London two centuries ago. It's very popular with younger bankers and stockbrokers, happy to queue for such delights as steak 'n' kidney pie, or a chop from the grill (from about £7) and steamed syrup pudding (£3), washed down with house wine at £14.25 a bottle. / www.simpsonstavern.co.uk; L only, closed Sat & Sun.

Singapore Garden NW6 £23*   ★

83a Fairfax Rd   7624 8233   8–2A

Tucked away in a Swiss Cottage backstreet, this Oriental stalwart is usually packed, thanks to its friendly style and superior cooking. The menu mixes together a wide variety of Malaysian and Singaporean dishes, with all but a few main courses costing £4-£10. House wine is £15 a bottle. / www.singaporegarden.co.uk; 11 pm, Fri-Sat 11.30 pm.

Sitaaray WC2 £25*   🅐★

167 Drury Ln   7269 6422   4–1C

This fun, Bollywood-themed Covent Garden Indian offers better food than you might expect. Its set-price formula is ideal for parties, but sadly a little outside our price bracket. At lunchtime or pre- or post-theatre, however – when the menu costs £14.95 – you can just about keep within our budget. With house wine at £5 a glass, this is far from being a bargain-basement destination, though. / www.sitaaray.com; 1 am.

(Ground Floor)
Smiths of Smithfield EC1 £18*   🅐

67-77 Charterhouse St   7251 7950   9–1A

There are four floors of dining possibilities at this impressively-converted Smithfield warehouse, but only the mega-popular ground floor bar (a key weekend brunch destination) is really within our budget. Breakfast-type dishes such as the full English (£7.50) are served all day, and there are also lunchtime 'market specials', such as bangers 'n' mash, pies and quiches (around £6). The house wine is £13.95 a bottle, or drink Smithfield lager at £3.30 a pint. / www.smithsofsmithfield.co.uk; L only.

Snazz Sichuan NW1 £22 A★

37 Chalton St   7388 0808   8–3C

If you enjoy dishes heavy with chilli oil and/or offal, you'll love the scary-sounding concoctions on offer at this Sichuan club/gallery/restaurant, near Euston. There's a budget lunch menu with dishes around £8, or you can dive into the à la carte and sample 'fire-exploded kidney flowers' at £8.80, or 'gong po intestines' at £9.80 (though sadly, at £16, the 'hot and numbing boiled fish' may take you over budget). A large supply of cooling drink is a necessity – drink Tsingtao (or house wine is £12). / www.newchinaclub.co.uk; 10.30 pm.

Soho Japan W1 £20

52 Wells St   7323 4661   2–1B

'Fitzrovia Japan' would be a more accurate name for this basic café with mismatched tables and cutlery, as it's tucked away north of Oxford Street. It's worth forgiving its geographical pretensions, though, as its large menu is well-produced, and comes at low prices. A pint of draft Kirin will set you back £4.20. / www.sohojapan.co.uk; 10.30 pm; closed Sat L & Sun.

Somerstown Coffee House NW1 £21

60 Chalton St   7691 9136   8–3C

In the middle of a housing estate near Euston, this French-run boozer styles itself a 'bistro pub'. A typical main dish would be a burger (£8), and perhaps a crème brûlée (£5) for pudding – the food is good, and the wine (from £14 a bottle) is excellent. So is the beer, and there are numerous bitters and lagers on tap. / www.somerstowncoffeehouse.com; 11 pm.

Sông Quê E2 £17 ★★

134 Kingsland Rd   7613 3222   1–2D

They don't seem to have spent much on staff training or interior décor at this basic Shoreditch canteen. That's probably a good thing, though, as it keeps its zesty Vietnamese scoff at brilliant prices: you could push the boat out here and still stay well within budget – most starters and main courses are around a fiver, and the house wine is £7 a bottle. / 11 pm.

Spacca Napoli W1 £20 A★

101 Dean St   7437 9440   3–1D

A great option either for a break from Oxford Street shopping, or for a budget night out in the West End – this packed Italian joint specialises in pizza 'al metro' (by the metre) which comes in at about £5–£9 per portion. There are also a wide range of cheaper antipasti, salads and pastas. A bottle of house vino costs £12.95. / www.spaccanapoli.co.uk; 11 pm.

Spago SW7 £17 ★

6 Glendower Pl   7225 2407   5–2B

Conveniently located two minutes' from the tube in pricey South Kensington, this well-established pizza joint offers good nosh without the price tag of some of its neighbours. Hearty pizza and pasta options are the way to go – starters cost around £4 and main dishes are from £6.50–£13.60. The house wine is £11.80 a bottle. / www.spagolondon.co.uk; midnight; no Amex.

Spianata & Co £ 11 ★

41 Brushfield St, E1   7655 4411   9–1D
20 Holborn Viaduct, EC1   7236 3666   9–2A
12 Moorfields, EC2   7638 6118   9–2C
29-30 Leadenhall Mkt, EC3   7929 1339   9–2C
73 Watling St, EC4   7236 3666   9–2B
This growing chain offers an Italian take on the soups, sarnies and salads formula (and is named for the 'Pizza Bianca Romana' bread used in its sandwiches). Prices (say £4.30 for a Prosciutto & Mozzarella) aren't dis-similar to the Prets of the world, and it makes a bit of a change. Unlicensed: soft drinks are a bit under £1. / www.spianata.com; L only; closed Sat & Sun, except E1 open Sun; no credit cards; no bookings.

Square Pie Company £ 12

Unit 9, The Brunswick Centre, WC1   7837 6207   8–4C
1 Canada Sq, Jubilee Line Mall, E14   7519 6071   11–1C
16 Horner St, Old Spitalfields Mkt, E1   7377 1114   9–1D
It does what it says on the tin at this small, no frills chain which patriots hail as a splendid take on British fast food. The pies themselves come in classic and midi sizes, with a variety of traditional and less traditional fillings: a classic steak & mushroom will set you back £4.95. The outlets are unlicensed, but do juices and smoothies for a little under £2. / www.squarepie.com; E14 4 pm -7 pm; E1 3 pm - 6 pm, W1 6 pm - 8 pm, WC1 10.30 pm; E1 closed Sat, E14 closed Sun; no bookings.

Sree Krishna SW17 £ 14 ★★

192-194 Tooting High St   8672 4250   10–2C
This Tooting veteran claims to have introduced southern Indian cuisine to the UK. The long menu divides between vegetarian and non-vegetarian dishes, and main courses range in price from £4-£8. On Sundays, there are also thali specials for £6.95 (veggie) and £8.95. Wash it all down with a bottle of house wine at £9.50 or a mango lassi (£2.50). / www.sreekrishna.co.uk; 10.45 pm, Fri & Sat midnight.

Star Café W1 £ 17

22 Gt Chapel St   7437 8778   3–1D
No-one would recommend this ancient Soho café (a cut above your typical greasy spoon) for gastronomy. For a decent fry-up, though, it's a favourite for many local ad-land executives – options start from a fiver. At other times of day, mains like steak & Guinness pie are £7.95, and apple crumble is £2.75. House wine is £12.95 a bottle. / www.thestarcafe.co.uk; L only, closed Sat & Sun; no Amex.

Stick & Bowl W8 £ 17 ★

31 Kensington High St   7937 2778   5–1A
The name says it all at this chaotic, ultra no-frills diners, which makes a good spot to eat and run in pricey Kensington, so long as you don't mind squeezing onto one of its few and uncomfortable perches. At the price, though, no-one's complaining, with most dishes (say beef with ginger & spring onions) for about a fiver. House wine is £2.20 a glass, or a can of Tsingtao will set you back £2.50. / 11 pm; no credit cards; no booking.

Stock Pot £11

40 Panton St, SW1   7839 5142   4–4A
18 Old Compton St, W1   7287 1066   4–2A
273 King's Rd, SW3   7823 3175   5–3C

These battered '60s-survivor bistros are the very essence of cheap 'n' cheerful. They may not offer gastronomy, but – with a 3-course set dinner for £7.80, and house wine at £9.20 a bottle – it's difficult not to warm to them, and they're still almost invariably packed. / 11.30 pm, Sun 10.30 pm; no credit cards.

Story Deli
The Old Truman Brewery E1 £21   A★

3 Dray Walk   7247 3137   1–2D

If you're hanging out around Brick Lane, this shabby chic café in the old brewery is just the spot for a quick bite, although its mad popularity means you may have to settle for a perch at the large communal table. All organic, paper-thin pizza is the thing, and though not of themselves that cheap (chorizo & aubergine, £11) they're packed with flavour. Go easy on the wine, though: the cheapest is £20 a bottle! / 9 pm during summer.

Stringray Globe Café E2 £14   ★

109 Columbia Rd   7613 1141   1–2D

If you need a break from the Columbia Road flower market, this trendy East End joint – a bar/café and pizzeria – is just the job. The menu majors in pizza and pasta for about £6, and with the former in particular you won't go hungry given the man-sized portions. There's a large wine list kicking off at £11 a bottle (as well as a good range of beers and cocktails). / www.stringraycafe.co.uk; 11 pm; no Amex.

Sugar Reef W1 £19*

42-44 Gt Windmill St   7851 0800   3–2D

No-one would hail this huge Soho venue as a great culinary destination. However, it does some substantial, early-week (Monday to Wednesday) lunch deals that are well worth knowing about, offering two courses for £12, three courses for £15. You might have Thai fish cakes, a lamb burger, then stocky toffee pudding & ice cream to finish. A bottle of house wine is £13.95. / www.sugarreef.co.uk; 1 am; D only, closed Sun.

Sushi-Say NW2 £17   ★

33b Walm Ln   8459 7512   1–1A

Willesden's Green's greatest claim to culinary fame can be found at the Shimizu family's charming fixture of a dozen years' standing – this is a Japanese restaurant worth crossing numerous postcodes for. Prices are not bargain-basement, but the sushi is some of the best in town – you can sample 8 pieces for £16, perhaps preceding it with seafood dumplings (£5.20). Drink a large bottle of Kirin for £4.90. / 10 pm, Sat & Sun 10.30 pm; closed Mon; no Amex.

Sweetings EC4 £14*   A

39 Queen Victoria St   7248 3062   9–3B

This one's a bit of a cheat – you couldn't accommodate the good-but-simple fish and seafood cooking at this ancient City institution within our budget. But if you're prepared to slum it standing at the bar with a generously-filled sandwich (about a fiver) and a bottle of the house wine (a hefty £19.50), you won't find a more characterful place for a convivial lunch. Don't forget to wear your pinstripes. / L only, closed Sat & Sun; no booking.

The Table SE1 £14

83 Southwark St 7401 2760 9–4B

An integral part of architectural practice Allied & Morrison, this smart canteen certainly scores highly for style. There's a good amount of substance in its menu too, though, be it for breakfast or a healthy lunch. For the latter, there's a large range of mix 'n' match salads (£1.45/100 grams), quality sarnies (around £2.50-£4.50) and some fantastic desserts (such as bread 'n' butter pudding for £2.50). Drink fresh lemonade (£1). / www.thetablecafe.com; L only.

Taiwan Village SW6 £21 ★★

85 Lillie Rd 7381 2900 5–3A

Both the Lillie Road and the North End Road are long streets lacking any reputation for good restaurants, so this excellent Taiwanese near the gyratory where they meet is doubly worth knowing about. Even if you think you know your stuff when it comes to regional Chinese dishes, the best option is often to 'leave it to the chef'. House wine is £12 a bottle. / www.taiwanvillage.com; 11.30 pm; closed Mon L.

Tajima Tei EC1 £24 ★

9-11 Leather Ln 7404 9665 9–2A

It may be hidden away, near Hatton Garden, but this high-quality Japanese restaurant is well worth seeking out. Set menus are always comforting if you're eating on a budget, and here you will find a wide range of bento and other set lunches from £10/head. There are set dinners from £15 too – à la carte, you could spend rather more. Wines from £12.50 a bottle. / www.tajima-tei.co.uk; 10 pm; closed Sat L & Sun.

Talad Thai SW15 £16 ★

320 Upper Richmond Rd 8789 8084 10–2A

The décor isn't long on luxury at this simple, communal-seating Thai canteen next to an Oriental supermarket of the same name on the fringe of Putney. The queues attest to its local popularity, however, and to the quality of its inexpensive scoff. Most dishes are a fiver or a little more, and the house wine is £13.50 a bottle. / www.taladthai.co.uk; 10.30 pm; no Amex.

Tampopo SW10 £20

140 Fulham Rd 7370 5355 5–3B

Londoners may think they know it all foodwise, but the Chelsea-fringe outlet of this Manchester-based pan-Oriental chain can show many of the locals a thing or two. It's a stylish and comfortable place, where few main courses are much more than a tenner, and the house wine comes at £12.95 a bottle. For the best value of all, seek out the express lunch menu (£6.95). / www.tampopo.co.uk; 11 pm, Fri-Sat 11.30 pm.

Tandoori Nights SE22 £22 🄰★

73 Lordship Ln 8299 4077 1–4D

Crowded and noisy, this popular East Dulwich Indian keeps the locals piling in for food that's several cuts above the norm. With curries around the £8 mark, you can eat within our budget at any time, but best value of all is the 2- and 3-course lunchtime menus (£9.95 and £12.95). A la carte prices are still within budget with starters such as subzi around £4 and mains around £9. A bottle of Cobra is £4.50. / 11.30 pm; closed weekday L & Sat L

Tangawizi TW1 £22 ★

406 Richmond Rd   8891 3737   1–4A

The odd East African influence adds interest to the light-tasting dishes of this friendly modern curry house in Twickenham, where main dishes other than seafood (and with many veggie options) are generally priced between £6–£9. The house wine is £11.95 – a small Cobra or Kingfisher £2.75. / www.tangawizi.co.uk; 10.30 pm; D only, closed Sun.

Tapas Brindisa SE1 £22

18-20 Southwark St   7357 8880   9–4C

In late-2008, the famous Spanish food-importers Brindisa opened two new spin-offs from their popular Borough Market tapas bar of which this smartly designed bar/café in the heart of Soho is one. Prices are hardly bargain-basement, but you can have an interesting meal here within our budget – perhaps cured beef & salad (£5.75) and steamed mussels (£5.40), followed by crema catalana & figs (£4). A top quality all-Spanish list starts at £14.95 a bottle. / www.brindisa.com; 11 pm; closed Sun.

Taqueria W11 £18 𝔸

139-143 Westbourne Grove   7229 4734   6–1B

Want to hang out with the Notting Hill trustafarians, but lack the requisite funds? No problem: head for this jolly Mexican café. Most of the tostados and tacos are not much more than a fiver, so you can be pretty sure of dining here within our budget, even if you succumb to a margharita (£6.85). A more economical choice on the drinks front is house wine at £15.50 a bottle. / www.coolchiletaqueria.co.uk; Mon-Thu 11 pm, Fri & Sat 11.30 pm, Sun 10.30 pm; no Amex; no booking.

Taro £15

10 Old Compton St, W1   7439 2275   4–2B

61 Brewer St, W1   7734 5826   3–2D

A cartoon of the proprietor, Mr Taro, provides the logo for this duo of busy Japanese canteens in Soho, and the man himself is often to be found presiding over his cheerful small kingdom. For a quick, cheap bite, this is an ideal destination. Single rice dishes are priced from about £6, and a plate of mixed sushi is £8.50. A bottle of Kirin is £2.50, green tea is £1, or a small hot sake is £3. / www.tarorestaurants.co.uk; 10.30 pm, Sun 9.30 pm; no Amex; Brewer St only small bookings.

Tartine SW3 £20 𝔸

114 Draycott Ave   7589 4981   5–2C

On a budget but still want to hang out with the South Kensington Euros? Head for this contemporary-style bistro, which specialises in toasties (made with bread from fabled Parisian bakery Poilâne). You can start the day here in real style with a scrambled egg and smoked salmon tartine (£8.70), or, later on, you might be ready for a shredded duck, crispy ginger, cucumber & plum sauce version (£10.75), or perhaps just a burger (£9.95). Wines kick off at £3.95 a glass. / www.tartine.co.uk; 11 pm; need 6+ to book at D.

Tas £17 𝔸

22 Bloomsbury St, WC1   7637 4555   2–1C
33 The Cut, SE1   7928 2111   9–4A
72 Borough High St, SE1   7403 7200   9–4C
37 Farringdon Rd, EC1   7430 9721   9–1A

These large and perennially buzzing Turkish eateries have made a big name as budget dining destinations, and they have perhaps become a touch complacent of late. With a good variety of set-price formulas (£8.95-£17.95), however, they're still very handy to know about, most particularly on theatre trips (and especially for groups). Most fun is to be had from the mezze, washed down with wines kicking off at £13.20 a bottle. / www.tasrestaurant.com; 11.30 pm.

Tawana W2 £19 ★

3 Westbourne Grove   7229 3785   6–1C

It's the good-value cooking, rather than any special charm of setting or service, which is the attraction of this busy and popular Thai, just off Queensway. Starters and main courses are generally around the £5-£7 mark, and the house wine is £11.95 a bottle. / www.tawana.co.uk; 11 pm.

Ten Ten Tei W1 £22 ★

56 Brewer St   7287 1738   3–2D

It's certainly no thanks to its looks that this scruffy Japanese dive in Soho is usually very busy (and generally with a reassuring Oriental-looking crowd too). It has a certain gritty, authentic charm, though, and with care, you can eat here within our budget at any time from the very extensive menu. Set menus include two courses along with rice and miso soup (ranging from £6.50-£12 for lunch and £18 dinner). House wine is £12 a bottle. / 10 pm; closed Sun; no Amex.

Tentazioni SE1 £16* ★★

2 Mill St   7394 5248   11–2A

It's rare to be able to include a restaurant of such high quality within a cheap eats guide. Fortunately for bargain-seekers, this fine Italian ten-year-old has such a tucked-away location (in a Bermondsey side street, near the Design Museum) it knows it has to offer a good deal to draw people in. The deal's not just good – it's brilliant – two courses including wine for £11.95: perhaps ravioli with spicy seafood, then grilled salmon with spinach & lentils. The Italian wine list is in the 'heavyweight' class, but starts at a reasonable £12.50 a bottle. / www.tentazioni.co.uk; 10.45 pm; closed Mon L, Sat L & Sun.

Terroirs WC2 £21* ★★

5 William IV St   7036 0660   4–4C

Why aren't there more places like this tremendous, late-2008 opening? Just a short walk from Charing Cross station, this is a no-fuss Gallic spot (with an English chef!) serving up simple but very appetising dishes – including charcuterie, cheeses and bistro classics – at reasonable prices. The well-chosen wine is much of the attraction, with options starting at £13.95 a bottle (£3.95 a glass). A daily lunch special (£10) includes a dish of the week and a glass of wine. / www.terroirswinebar.com; 11 pm; closed Sun.

Thai Café SW1 £18
22 Charlwood St   7592 9584   2–4C
They don't stand much on ceremony at this Pimlico corner café, but – the area hardly being awash with tolerable places to eat, at any price level – it attracts a steady following with its menu of Oriental staples at reasonable prices. Most starters are around the £4-£5 mark, and most main courses around £5-£8. A bottle of house wine is £11.55 or have Thai beer for £2.95 a bottle. / 10.30 pm; closed Sat L & Sun L.

Thai Corner Café SE22 £18 ★
44 North Cross Rd   8299 4041   1–4D
This packed local café is a staple venue for East Dulwich locals enjoying a casual evening out that doesn't break the bank – main dishes range from £5.45-£8.50, with starters around £4 and desserts for £2.50. A large part of the appeal is that you can BYO (£2 corkage). / 10.30 pm; no credit cards.

Thai Garden SW11 £17
58 Battersea Rise   7738 0380   10–2C
This airy Battersea Thai has earned its stripes with consistently good cooking over many years. Service is friendly too, so it's worth checking out the long menu, which offers extensive permutations of the standard repertoire – most curries are around the £7 mark, and the house wine is £12.25 a bottle. / www.thaigarden.co.uk; 11 pm; D only.

Thailand SE14 £19
15 Lewisham Way   8691 4040   1–3D
Despite its unpropitious New Cross location, this Oriental café has carved out quite a reputation over the years for its interesting Thai/Laotian cooking. You could visit any time and sample it within our budget, but for value-hounds there's a great lunchtime 2-course deal, which runs till 7pm – for just £3.95, you might have chicken tom yum and a green curry. Stay away from the collection of 150 whiskies, and you can drink cheaply too, with wines starting at £10.95 a bottle. / 11.30 pm.

The Thatched House W6 £21 Ⓐ
115 Dalling Rd   8748 6174   7–1B
Hammersmith is well off for pubs aiming to dazzle with their cooking. This comfortably modernised hostelry – with a good-sized, tented garden in summer – isn't one of them. That's not to say the food here's bad, just that it's not aiming for fireworks – think filled ciabattas with chips and salad (about £6), or a similarly garnished burger for around a tenner. Drink house wine at £14.50 a bottle, or a pint of Fosters for £3.90. / www.thatchedhouse.com; 10 pm; no Amex.

Toff's N10 £16 ★
38 Muswell Hill Broadway   8883 8656   1–1B
Trying to park near this acclaimed Muswell Hill chippy can be a bit of nightmare, but fans say the fantastic fish justifies the hassle. Haddock 'n' chips will set you back £10.95 if you eat in, and if you've room for soup of the day to start it's £4.50. The lunch special (offered from 11.30am-5pm) includes cod 'n' chips with bread and butter and tea or coffee for £8.95. House wine is £3.45 a glass. / www.toffsfish.co.uk; 10 pm; closed Sun; no booking, Sat.

Tokyo City EC2   **£18**   ★

46 Gresham St   7726 0308   9–2B

Handily located for a light City lunch – not far from the Bank
of England – this Japanese snackery offers budget possibilities such
as bento boxes (£7.50-£13.50) or sushi (£1.60-£2.95 a piece),
with house wine at £10.80 a bottle. As is often the way with
Japanese places, you could also spend a lot more if you wanted to.
/ 10 pm; closed Sat & Sun.

Tokyo Diner WC2   **£16**

2 Newport Pl   7287 8777   4–3B

Why did Richard Hill locate his noon-midnight, 365-days-a-year
Japanese diner in the heart of Chinatown? We don't know. But for
a simple, cheap snack, this small, basic looking dive fits the bill nicely.
A wide range of inexpensive lunch set deals range from £5.90,
and bento box meals at other times of day from £10.50. Drink wine
at £6.90 a bottle or – more authentically – sake from £2.90 a glass.
No tipping. / www.tokyodiner.com; 11.30 pm; no Amex; no booking, Fri & Sat.

Tom Ilic SW8   **£23***   ★

123 Queenstown Rd   7622 0555   10–1C

Tom Ilic is a chef with quite a name for his uncompromising style
of cuisine, and the à la carte prices at his Battersea restaurant are,
unsurprisingly, rather out of our price-bracket. You can, however,
check out his ambitious 2-course lunch menu for just £12.50. Your
selection might be baked sea bass with potato, mussels & garlic
cream, followed by white chocolate & Mascarpone cheesecake with
poached rhubarb. Wines kick off at £14.75 a bottle. / www.tomilic.com;
10.30 pm; closed Mon, Tue L, Sat L & Sun D.

Tom's Deli W11   **£15***   𝔸

226 Westbourne Grove   7221 8818   6–1B

Expect to queue if you want to brunch with the beautiful crowd
at Tom Conran's deli/café in the heart of Notting Hill. There are
cheaper ways to start the day, but few more fashionable. A full
English is £9, and there are sarnies from a fiver, or quiche of the day
for £8. It's not a boozy kind of place – a fresh juice is £2 – but if you
ask nicely they may let you BYO for modest corkage.
/ www.tomsdelilondon.co.uk; 7.30 pm, Sat & Sun 6.30 pm; L only; no Amex;
no booking.

Tong Ka Nom Thai NW10   **£16**   ★

833 Harrow Rd   8964 5373   1–2A

The dining room is small and not particularly comfortable at this
homespun venture between Kensal Rise and Willesden. No one who
visits is looking for style points, though, but rather the excellent Thai
cooking, whose good-value is boosted by the ability to BYO as the
place is unlicensed. Main dishes range from £5.20-£6.80, making
a meal here at any time well within our price limit.

Tosa W6   **£14***   ★★

332 King St   8748 0002   7–2B

This Japanese spot near Stamford Brook tube isn't a glamour
location, but does what it does (most notably yakitori) extremely well.
Best value is to be had from the lunchtime menu, which offers
a small dish such as edamame and a main dish of sashimi for £10.
At other times, you'd have to choose reasonably carefully from the
wide ranging menu, which includes sushi, to stay within our budget.
For maximum economy, you can of course drink tea, or instead have
Sapporo for £3. / 11 pm; no Amex.

sign up for the survey at hardens.com

Trinity Stores SW12   £14   Ⓐ
5-6 Balham Station Rd   8673 3773   10–2C
Any neighbourhood would be happy to have this excellent little
deli/café, but in Balham it seems verging on the miraculous, with its
fresh-tasting, simple snacks. A dish like home made soup is £4,
some quiche with salad goes for £4.95. They've also put some effort
into their wine selection, which starts at £11.95 a bottle.
/ www.trinitystores.co.uk; 8pm, Sat 5.30 pm, Sun 4 pm; L only; no Amex.

Trojka NW1   £18
101 Regent's Park Rd   7483 3765   8–4A
This cosy all-day Russian tea room – and you don't see many of those
– is a useful find in chichi Primrose Hill (and live music sometimes
adds to its attraction). You could eat from its vast menu or take tea
here anytime within budget, but they do a notably keenly priced 2-
course weekday lunch deal. For £9.95 you might have herring fillet
to start and Ukranian beef goulash to finish. House wine is £10.95
a bottle, or try the Russian beer at £2.90. / www.trojka.co.uk; 10.30 pm.

Troubadour SW5   £19   Ⓐ
263-267 Old Brompton Rd   7370 1434   5–3A
In spite of expansion over the years, this Earl's Court coffee shop has
famously retained much of its Bohemian charm. At the culinary level,
it's really only for breakfast (try the 'Anti Heart Attack' with fresh
fruit, Greek yoghurt, honey, and toast, £7.75) that it can really
be recommended, but light dishes are available all day. Especially
if eating alone, appropriate reading matter – foreign-language
newspapers, Nietzsche and so on – is de rigueuer.
/ www.troubadour.co.uk; 11.30 pm; no Amex.

La Trouvaille W1   £23*   Ⓐ★
12a Newburgh St   7287 8488   3–2C
This excellent French institution, off Carnaby Street, certainly is a
'find'. Ignore the restaurant (it's good, but too pricey), and head
instead for the basement bar, where friendly staff dispense a notably
good wine list starting at £16 per bottle. The food is far from
incidental, though, with simple dishes like croque & fries (£6.95)
alongside foie gras platters at £8.75. To finish, polish off a crème
brûlée for £4.95. / www.latrouvaille.co.uk; 11 pm; closed Sun.

Two Brothers N3   £19   ★
297-303 Regent's Park Rd   8346 0469   1–1B
The Manzis have sold out, so it's two new brothers – Mal and Nari
Atwal – who now preside at this famous North Finchley chippy. The
menu is fancier nowadays, with cod 'n' chips (£11.75) now sitting
alongside such non-budget suggestions as grilled black cod in a
caramelised pepper sauce (£14.95), but standards remain high,
and wines (starting off at £12.50 a bottle) are still relatively
reasonably priced. / www.twobrothers.co.uk; 10.15 pm; closed Mon & Sun;
no booking at D.

Uli W11   £18   Ⓐ★
16 All Saints Rd   7727 7511   6–1B
For a combination of charm, interesting cooking and economy at any
time of day, it's hard to beat this south east Asian café in one
of Notting Hill's hippest restaurant streets. For the summer, there's
even a pleasant courtyard at the rear. On the menu you might find
the likes of five-spice pork rolls (£5.75), vegetable tempura (£4.50)
and shredded chilli beef (£7.75), washed down with house wine
at £10.95 a bottle. / www.uli-Oriental.co.uk; 11 pm; D only, closed Sun;
no Amex.

Vapiano W1 £19

19-21 Great Portland St   7268 0080   3–1C

Don't get too excited by the culinary prospects at this first UK branch of a major German chain. Unless, that is, you like the idea of taking a swipe card with you from station to station to get your dishes. This place is just a stone's throw from Oxford Circus, though, and can be handy for a shopping lunch or before a show at the Palladium. It offers a wide range of salads (such as Caprese, £5), pizza and pasta (around £7.50), and puddings (around £3.75). House wine is £11.50 for a bottle. / www.vapiano.co.uk; 11 pm.

El Vergel SE1 £12 ★★

8 Lant St   7357 0057   9–4B

Few places inspire love like this zesty Latino café, hidden in an obscure Borough backstreet. You do have to cram yourself in to a packed canteen setting, but it's well worth it for outstanding South American fare at brilliant prices (emapanadas £2.70, tortilla salad £4.70, smoked salmon & gaucamole £3.90, halva, semolina & almond cake £1.30). Wine is just £8.50 a bottle, or drink San Miguel at £2.30. Now if they only opened in the evenings... / www.elvergel.co.uk; breakfast & L only, closed Sat D & Sun; no credit cards.

Viet W1 £12 ★

34 Greek St   7494 9888   4–3A

You don't get much in the way of creature comforts or pampering at this basic Soho Oriental. For a quick hit of punchy, fresh flavours, though, it hits the bill and at very good prices, with a noodle dish typically about £6. You can BYO (corkage £2.50). / 11 pm, Fri 11.30 pm; no Amex.

Viet Garden N1 £15

207 Liverpool Rd   7700 6040   8–2D

It can be tough to nab a table at this popular Islington pit stop, which is well-known locally for its appetising Vietnamese scoff at good prices, with most dishes costing £3-£8. Leave space for some fried coconut-wrapped ice cream (£3.50). House wine is £9.95 a bottle. / www.vietgarden.co.uk; 11 pm; no Amex.

Vijay NW6 £18 ★★

49 Willesden Ln   7328 1087   1–1B

This quirky and popular '60s Kilburn Indian hasn't changed much over the years, and even the prices seem reluctant to acknowledge the passing of the years. Southern Indian vegetarian dishes, such as dosas (potato & lentil pancakes, £6.20) are something of a speciality, but more standard meaty curries (£6-£8) are also available. The house wine is £12 a bottle. / www.vijayindia.com; 10.45 pm, Fri-Sat 11.30 pm.

Vijaya Krishna SW17 £17

114 Mitcham Rd   8767 7688   10–2C

The Keralan (south Indian) cuisine is typically good – and can be outstanding – at this Tooting curry house, where a dish like masala dosa is £3.90, and even a pricier option like Cochin prawn curry is still only £6.90. House wine comes in at £9.90 a bottle. / 11 pm, Fri & Sat midnight; no Amex.

Villa Bianca NW3 £21*
1 Perrins Ct   7435 3131   8–2A
Thanks to one of the cutest locations in town – a picturesque cobbled alley off Hampstead High Street – this datedly glamorous Italian can normally charge prices well out of reach of our budget. Not so at lunch though, when there's a 2-course menu for £12.90. You might have a pasta dish to start, and liver with fried onions & bacon as a main dish, washed down with house wine at £13.90 a bottle. / www.villabiancanw3.com; 11.30 pm.

Village East SE1 £19* A★
171-173 Bermondsey St   7357 6082   9–4D
As a name nodding to NYC's East Village implies, this large Bermondsey bar/restaurant is – by night – a self-consciously hip destination (and by no means a budget one). By day, the trendiness is turned down a notch or two, and there's a 2-course set menu that's well worth seeking out – for £13, you might enjoy the likes of salmon gravadlax followed by risotto of mushroom, washed down with a glass of house wine for £3.80. / www.villageeast.co.uk; 10 pm, Sun 9.30 pm.

Vincent Rooms
Westminster Kingsway College SW1 £19
Vincent Sq   7802 8391   2–4C
There's an element of Russian roulette when you eat at this large and attractive Westminster dining room, where guests double up as guinea pigs for the trainee chefs and waiting staff of the adjoining catering college (where St Jamie once trained). One thing you can be sure of is that – given the level of ambition of the food – prices are very reasonable. Starters and desserts are around £4, main courses £8-£9, and house wine £10 a bottle. / www.thevincentrooms.com; 9 pm; times vary; only term times; closed Mon D, Wed D, Fri D, Sat & Sun; no Amex.

Vrisaki N22 £25* ★
73 Myddleton Rd   8889 8760   1–1C
The budget isn't all that's going to be bursting after a meal to this long-running Bound's Green taverna. Given the generosity of its massive mezze deal (£18 per person), you're unlikely to finish without having to loosen your belt several notches. NB You'd have to stick to a single glass of wine (£2.95) to have any hope of staying roughly within our price limit. / midnight, Sun 9 pm.

Wahaca £19 A
66 Chandos Pl, WC2   7240 1883   4–4C
Ariel Way, W12   8749 4517   7–1C
This Covent Garden basement Mexican has made quite a splash, and it's often difficult to get a table. Options range from tacos (pork pibil is £3.75) up to more substantial dishes like enchilada verde – spicy chicken, in tomatillo sauce with cheese – for £8.50. Wine starts at £12.50 a bottle. There is a new branch in the Westfield development in Shepherd's Bush, but it somewhat lacks the zest of the original. / www.wahaca.com.

The Walmer Castle W11 £21 A
58 Ledbury Rd   7229 4620   6–1B
If you want to hang with the younger Notting Hillbillies, this friendly first-floor Thai dining room above a perennially hip pub is the place for you. Prices are reasonable, with starters and desserts around the £5.50 mark and main courses about £7.50 – a typical selection might be satay followed by chicken & cashew stir-fry. House wine starts at £3.85 a glass. / 10.30 pm; D only, ex Fri & Sat open L & D.

White Horse SW6   **£19**

1-3 Parsons Grn   7736 2115   10-1B

Still better known to many as the 'Sloaney Pony', this large Fulham pub has much to interest the budget gastronome, though much of it of an alcoholic nature, as it maintains an excellent wine list (starting at £12.50 a bottle) and one of the finest ranges of real ales in town (typical is Adnams at £2.75 a pint). The solid nourishment ain't at all bad, though, with a typical meal comprising beer-battered haddock (£10.25), followed by chocolate torte (£4.50). / www.whitehorsesw6.com; 10.30 pm.

Whits W8   **£24***   ★

21 Abingdon Rd   7938 1122   5-1A

Notably charming service adds to the experience at this small but winning little local, just off Kensington High Street. The quality of the cooking is high with prices typically out of reach of this guide, so it's well worth knowing about their Wednesday-Friday lunch deal. For £15.50 you get two courses, which might be lobster tartelette, followed by rib eye steak & chips, with béarnaise sauce. A carafe of house wine is £10. / www.whits.co.uk; 10.30 pm; closed Mon, Tue-Sat D only, closed Sun D.

William IV NW10   **£20**   A★

786 Harrow Rd   8969 5944   1-2B

Offering substantial tapas for around £6 each, this large and rambling Kensal Green boozer makes an affordable place for a light and convivial meal at any time (and even more so for weekday lunches when they do a 3-for-2 deal). There's a wide range of lagers and bitters of course (from £3 a pint), and also a very decent range of Old and New World wines, kicking off at £13 a bottle. / www.williamivlondon.com; 10.30 pm, Fri & Sat 11 pm, Sun 9.30 pm.

The Windsor Castle W8   **£19**   A

114 Campden Hill Rd   7243 8797   6-2B

Foodies should probably skip this entry, as the pub grub at this Georgian tavern near Notting Hill Gate (named for the view it enjoyed long ago) is not its main attraction. Few London pubs, however, can rival the quaint charms of its intriguing panelled interior and cute walled garden. A small glass of wine is just £2.85, a pint of London Pride is £2.85, and to help soak 'em up order the likes of sausage 'n' mash, or fish 'n' chips for £8.50. / www.windsorcastlepub.co.uk; 10 pm; no booking.

Wine Factory W11   **£22**

294 Westbourne Grove   7229 1877   6-1B

As the name suggests, the food isn't a big deal at this sparsely furnished Notting Hill bistro. But it's perfectly OK cheap 'n' cheerful scoff, such as fish soup £4.50, home-roasted ham £10, and there's usually a range of pizzas. The main event, though, is John Brinkley's hallmark great-value wine list, with options ranging from just £10 a bottle. / www.brinkleys.com; 11 pm; closed Sun D.

Wine Gallery SW10   **£20**   A

49 Hollywood Rd   7352 7572   5-3B

John Brinkley's long-established Chelsea-fringe bistro, slightly off the main drag, remains a bit of a locals' secret. The fodder – the likes of deep-fried brie & cranberry sauce (£5.50) followed by cottage pie with peas (£9.50) – isn't the main event: it's the super-bargain wine that keeps fans loyal. One bottle we checked at random was £11.50 here... and £29.50 at a restaurant not so far away in the King's Road! / www.brinkleys.com; 11.30 pm; closed Sun D; booking: max 12.

Wódka W8 £23*
12 St Alban's Grove   7937 6513   5–1B
It has a very picturesque location in a leafy Kensington backstreet, and this long-established venture offers Polish cooking prepared with more flair than possibly anywhere else in town; most inexpensively at lunchtime, when there's a 2-course set lunch for £14.50. You can drink wine (£14.50), but why would you miss the place's encyclopaedic list of vodkas? Sampling them is dangerously affordable at just £2.50 a pop. / www.wodka.co.uk; 11.15 pm; closed Sat L & Sun L

The Wolseley W1 £18*   Ⓐ
160 Piccadilly   7499 6996   3–3C
This dazzling, A-lister haunt – a grand Continental-style café near the Ritz – is a people-watcher's delight. Though it's not actually that expensive, its menu is generally beyond our price limit. At breakfast, however, it's just as popular, with just as starry a crowd, yet priced at a very affordable level: you'd generally escape for £10-£15 a head. They also make a feature of afternoon tea. If you want to go for either occasion, though, make sure you book. / www.thewolseley.com; midnight, Sun 11 pm.

Wong Kei W1 £10
41-43 Wardour St   7437 8408   4–3A
"Upstairs!" – the infamous greeting (if you're a Westerner, anyhow) at this bustling, five-storey Chinatown classic, whose regulars like to debate whether the waiters are getting any less rude over time (and whether they ham it up for effect). Whatever the story, this is one of the capital's classic cheap eats, with steaming bowls of tasty chow typically costing between £4-£5. House wine is £8 a bottle. / 11 pm; no credit cards; no booking.

Woo Jung WC2 £15   ★
56 Giles High St   7936 3103   4–1B
It certainly isn't the charm of the setting which draws people to this small Korean restaurant near Centre Point. Some (only) of the staff speak good English, though, helping you explore what might otherwise seem an impenetrable menu. Quality varies, but the prices encourage experimentation – we especially like the dish where the beef arrives raw with an egg on top, but is cooked in front of you by the heat of the stone bowl in which it is served. House wine is £9.50 a bottle.

Woodlands £17*
37 Panton St, SW1   7839 7258   4–4A
77 Marylebone Ln, W1   7486 3862   2–1A
102 Heath St, NW3   7794 3080   8–1A
It's pricey à la carte, but the lunchtime and pre-theatre buffet (£9.95-£12.95 with a drink) at the very central West End branch of this international chain of veggie Indians (also with branches in India and Singapore) offers good value. The house wine is £13.50 a bottle. / www.woodlandsrestaurant.co.uk; 10.45 pm; W4 Mon-Thu D only.

World Food Café WC2 £15
First Floor, 14 Neal's Yd   7379 0298   4–2C
This long-running Covent Garden café may be hidden away, overlooking Neal's Yard, but it's worth discovering when you need a budget bite. It serves a small menu of quality, filling scoff. Typical options include a Mexican plate (£7.95) or an Indian masala plate (£6.95). Puddings, such as chocolate cake, are £2.95. Drink fresh juices from £1.95. / L only, closed Sun; no Amex; no booking.

Yauatcha W1 £23* ★★

Broadwick Hs, 15-17 Broadwick St   7494 8888   3–2D

Alan Yau's moody Soho basement is one of the trendiest Chinese joints in town, and if you don't tread cautiously you could easily blow double the budget here. Thanks to its dim sum formula, however, if you pick with reasonable care you can keep costs under control with dishes starting from just £3. You might have shitake & duck roll (£3.80), with shredded chicken (£6.50), plus pork & prawn shumai (dumplings, £3.90), fried squid cake (£4) and sticky rice in lotus leaf (£3.90). House wine starts at a hefty £6.40 a glass, so drink Yebisu beer at £4 a bottle. / www.yauatcha.com; 11.30 pm.

Yelo £14

136a Lancaster Rd, W11   7243 2220   6–1A
8-9 Hoxton Sq, N1   7729 4626   9–1D

A small chain of Oriental noodle cafés, of which the Hoxton branch is perhaps most worth remembering thanks to its good location with numerous al fresco tables right on Hoxton Square. With starters from £3.95 and main curry, stir-fry and noodle dishes priced from £5.45 you don't have to work hard to stay within our price limit here. Drink Tiger beer at £2.75 per bottle. / www.yelothai.com; N1 11 pm, Sun - Mon 10.30 pm, W1 10.30 pm; need 6+ to book.

Yi-Ban £18* ★

Imperial Wharf, Imperial Rd, SW6   7731 6606   5–4B
Regatta Centre, Dockside Rd, E16   7473 6699   11–1D

For a bit of an adventure, seek out the east London original branch of this Chinese duo, on the first floor of an imposing riverside building (and offering fine views of the comings and goings at City Airport). It's quite a smart destination too, with a long, medium-priced menu. The real culinary attraction, however, is the extensive dim sum menu (most dishes £2.30-£3.50) available until 5pm, washed down with house wine at £12 a bottle. The Fulham branch – in an anonymous riverside development – is quite good too, but much less interesting. / www.yi-ban.co.uk; 10.45 pm; SW6 closed Sun; minimum £10.

Yming W1 £18* ★★

35-36 Greek St   7734 2721   4–2A

Some of the best Chinese food in central London is to be found just outside Chinatown at Christine Yau's excellent and civilised Soho Oriental. A full meal here might slip outside our budget, but you can keep to it if you visit from noon-6pm, when for £10 you can have three courses – perhaps crispy wun tun, then chicken in hot sesame sauce, followed by lychees & longan fruit. House wine is just £12 a bottle, or drink Tsingtao beer at £2.80 a go. / www.yminglondon.com; 11.45 pm; closed Sun.

Yoshino W1 £16* ★

3 Piccadilly Pl   7287 6622   3–3D

You may be a stone's throw from Piccadilly Circus, but this small café feels every bit like somewhere in Tokyo. A la carte prices are a little outside our range, but if you stick to one of the wide range of bento boxes (£5.80-£19.80) – for example, the £9.80 box contains sashimi, tofu, grilled fish and a sweet omelette, accompanied by rice, vegetables, pickles & miso soup – you can stay happily within our limit. House wine is £15.50 a bottle, or you can drink unlimited Japanese tea for £1. / www.yoshino.net; 9 pm; closed Sun.

Yum Yum N16 £19 A★
187 Stoke Newington High St   7254 6751   1–1D
Stoke Newington has its fair share of good places, but there's nothing else for miles around like this huge, mega-popular Thai venue. You could eat here any time within budget, but the keenest deal is the 2-course set lunch for £7.95. Wine is a reasonable £12.50 a bottle, or there's a wide range of Oriental beers at the £3.30 mark. / www.yumyum.co.uk; 11 pm, Fri & Sat midnight.

Yuzu NW6 £17 ★
102 Fortune Green Rd   7431 6602   1–1B
The service is not always the strongest point of this tiny Japanese outfit in West Hampstead. The reason to seek it out, however, is its excellent food: in particular sushi, with 4 cut rolls typically costing about £4. A dish like mixed vegetable tempura is £6. Drink Asahi beer at £2.50 for a 330 ml bottle, or try a sake cocktail for £4.25. / www.yuzu-restaurants.com; 10.30 pm, Sun 10 pm; D only, closed Mon.

Zero Degrees SE3 £22 A
29-31 Montpelier Vale   8852 5619   1–4D
A Blackheath microbrewery with good-looking, 'industrial' modern décor, and where a pint of the excellent home-brew starts at £2.80 (with house wine at £12.25). From a wide-ranging menu, the top tip is the range of pizzas from the wood-burning oven, priced from £7-£9. The moules frites here are also good, but at £12.50 a plate tend to stretch the budget. / www.zerodegrees.co.uk; 11.30 pm, Sun 10.30 pm; no trainers.

INDEXES

BREAKFAST
(WITH OPENING TIMES)

Central
Abokado *(8)*
Amato *(8, Sun 9)*
Apostrophe: *Barrett St W1, Tott' Ct Rd W1, WC2 (7)*
Bar Italia *(7)*
Bistro 1: *Beak St W1 (Sun 11)*
Café in the Crypt *(Mon-Sat 8)*
Caffé Vergnano: *WC2 (8, Sun 11)*
Crussh: *W1 (7)*
Eagle Bar Diner *(Sat 10, Sun 11)*
Flat White *(8, Sat & Sun 9)*
La Fromagerie Café *(Mon 10.30, Tue-Fri 8, Sat 9, Sun 10)*
Fuzzy's Grub: *SW1 (7)*
Galvin at Windows *(7)*
Gordon's Wine Bar *(Mon-Fri 8)*
Konditor & Cook: *WC1 (9.30); W1 (9.30, Sun 10.30)*
Leon: *WC2 (7.30, Sat 9, Sun 10); Gt Marlborough St W1 (9.30, Sat & Sun 10.30)*
Maison Bertaux *(8.30, Sun 9)*
Monmouth Coffee Company: *WC2 (8)*
Nordic Bakery *(Mon - Fri 10)*
Le Pain Quotidien: *Marylebone High St W1 (7, Sat & Sun 8); Great Marlborough St W1 (8, Sat & Sun 9)*
Paul: *WC2 (7.30); W1 (7.30, Sat & Sun 8)*
Providores (Tapa Room) *(9, Sat & Sun 10)*
Pure California: *WC1 (7, Sat 8); Goodge St W1 (8); Beak St W1 (8, Sat 10)*
Ranoush: *SW1 (noon)*
Salade: *W1 (7.30)*
Star Café *(7)*
Stock Pot: *SW1 (7); W1 (9)*
The Wolseley *(7, Sat & Sun 8)*

West
Napket: *SW3 (8)*
Del'Aziz: *SW6 (7, Sun 7.30)*
Adams Café *(7.30, Sat 8.30)*
Bedlington Café *(8)*
Beirut Express: *W2 (7)*
Café Laville *(10, Sat & Sun 9)*

Chelsea Bun Diner *(7, Sun 9)*
Crussh: *W8 (7.30); W12 (8)*
Fresco *(8)*
Gail's Bread: *all branches (7, Sat & Sun 8)*
Hammersmith Café *(9)*
High Road Brasserie *(7, Sat & Sun 8)*
Kensington Square Kitchen *(8.30)*
Leon: *SW3 (8, Sat 9, Sun 10)*
Lisboa Pâtisserie *(7)*
Lucky Seven *(Tue - Sun 10)*
Mona Lisa *(7)*
Le Pain Quotidien: *SW3 (7, Sat & Sun 8); W8 (7.30, Sat & Sun 8)*
Pappa Ciccia: *Fulham High St SW6 (7.30)*
Paul: *SW7 (7)*
Ranoush: *W2 (10); SW3, W8 (noon)*
Stock Pot: *SW3 (8)*
Tartine *(11)*
Tom's Deli *(8, Sun 9)*
Troubadour *(9)*
White Horse *(9.30)*
Wine Factory *(Sat 11)*

North
The Almeida *(9, summer only)*
Banners *(9, Sat & Sun 10)*
Café Mozart *(9)*
Camino *(8, Sun 11)*
Chamomile *(7, Sun 8)*
Gail's Bread: *all branches (7, Sat & Sun 8)*
Gallipoli: *Upper St N1, Upper St N1 (10.30)*
Kenwood (Brew House) *(9)*
The Lansdowne *(Sat-Sun 10)*
Le Pain Quotidien: *NW1 (Sat 5, Sun 6)*
Paul: *NW3 (7, Sat & Sun 7.30)*
Sabor *(11)*
Trojka *(9)*

South
Amano Café: *Victor Wharf, Clink St SE1 (7, Sat & Sun 9)*
Boiled Egg & Soldiers *(9)*
The Duke's Head *(10, Sun noon)*
Esca *(8, Sat & Sun 9)*
Green & Blue *(9, Sun 11)*
Lola Rojo *(Sat & Sun 11)*

Monmouth Coffee Company: *SE1 (7.30)*
Le Pain Quotidien: *SE1 (8, Sun 9)*
Putney Station *(Sat & Sun 11)*
El Rincón Latino *(Sat & Sun 11)*
The Table *(7.30, Sat & Sun 9)*
Tapas Brindisa *(Fri & Sat 9)*
Tate Modern (Level 7) *(10)*
Trinity Stores *(8, Sat 9.30, Sun 10)*
El Vergel *(8.30, Sat 10.30)*

East
Chop'd: *EC3 (7)*
Ambassador *(8.30, Sat & Sun 11)*
Apostrophe: *all east branches (7)*
Brick Lane Beigel Bake *(24 hrs)*
Club Mangia *(7.30)*
Cock Tavern *(6)*
Crussh: *One Canada Sq E14, EC3 (7); Unit 21 Jubilee Pl E14, EC4 (7.30)*
Fuzzy's Grub: *EC2, Cornhill EC3, Fleet St EC4, Well Ct EC4 (7)*
Hilliard *(8)*
Kipferl *(8, Sat & Sun 9)*
Leon: *Ludgate Circus EC4 (8); E1 (8, Sat 9, Sun 10)*
Paul: *EC4 (7)*
E Pellicci *(7)*
Pinchito *(10)*
The Place Below *(7.30)*
St John Bread & Wine *(9, Sat & Sun 10)*
Salade: *Old Bailey EC4 (7.30); Fetter Ln EC4 (8)*
Smiths (Ground Floor) *(7, Sat 10, Sun 9.30)*
Spianata & Co: *E1, EC2, EC3, EC4 (7.30)*
Square Pie Company: *E14 (7)*

BYO
(BRING YOUR OWN WINE)

Central
Food for Thought
Fryer's Delight
Golden Hind
India Club
Joy King Lau
Paolina Café
Ragam
Rock & Sole Plaice

Seafresh
Viet
World Food Café

West
Adams Café
Alounak: all branches
Bedlington Café
Best Mangal
Blue Elephant
Café 209
Chelsea Bun Diner
Costa's Fish Restaurant
Five Hot Chillies
Hammersmith Café
Kandoo
Mohsen
Osteria Basilico
Pappa Ciccia: Munster Rd SW6
The Red Pepper
Rôtisserie Jules: SW7
Satay House

North
Ali Baba
Diwana Bhel-Poori House
Geeta
Trojka
Vijay

South
Amaranth
Fish Club
Hot Stuff
The Table
Thai Corner Café

East
Lahore Kebab House
Mangal Ocakbasi
New Tayyabs
E Pellicci
The Place Below

Sakonis: *SW17 (h)*
The Sea Cow *(hmp)*
The Ship *(h)*
Sree Krishna *(h)*
The Table *(h)*
Tandoori Nights *(p)*
Tas: *all south branches (h)*
Tate Modern (Level 7) *(hmo)*
Tentazioni *(hp)*
Thai Corner Café *(h)*
Tom Ilic *(h)*
Trinity Stores *(hmp)*
Zero Degrees *(hp)*

East
Pho: *EC1 (ho)*
Alba *(hp)*
Ambassador *(mo)*
Il Bordello *(h)*
Cây Tre *(hm)*
Chi Noodle & Wine Bar *(p)*
Club Mangia *(hp)*
Crussh: *Unit 21 Jubilee Pl E14 (h)*
The Drunken Monkey *(p)*
Faulkner's *(hm)*
54 Farringdon Road *(hp)*
Fish Central *(m)*
The Fox *(p)*
The Gaylord *(p)*
Gourmet Burger Kitchen: *all branches (hp)*
Haz: *all branches (hp)*
Hilliard *(p)*
Itsu: *all branches (h)*
Kasturi *(hm)*
Lahore Kebab House *(h)*
Leon: *E1 (h)*
Moro *(h)*
Namo *(ehm)*
New Tayyabs *(h)*
E Pellicci *(pm)*
La Porchetta Pizzeria: *all branches (hp)*
The Quality Chop House *(hp)*
Royal China: *E14 (h)*
St John *(h)*
St John Bread & Wine *(h)*
Smiths (Ground Floor) *(hp)*

Sông Quê *(hp)*
Square Pie Company: *all east branches (m)*
Story Deli *(o)*
Stringray Globe Café *(hm)*
Tas: *EC1 (h)*
Yi-Ban: *E16 (h)*

ENTERTAINMENT
(CHECK TIMES BEFORE YOU GO)

Central
Café du Jardin
(jazz pianist, Wed-Sat)
Café in the Crypt
(jazz, Wed night)
Ciao Bella
(pianist, nightly)
Eagle Bar Diner
(DJ, Wed-Sat)
The Electric Birdcage
(DJ, percussionist on occasion)
Red Fort
(DJ, Thu-Sat)
Sugar Reef
(live music, Thu-Fri)

West
Del'Aziz: *SW6*
(belly dancer, Thu-Sat, live jazz, Tue in deli)
Azou
(belly dancer, Fri; live music, Sun)
Da Mario
(disco, Wed-Sat; magician, Wed)
Kensington Square Kitchen
(DJ, occasional weekends)
Lowiczanka
(live music, Sat)
Il Pagliaccio
(magician, Sun; salsa nights; jazz, weekly; opera, monthly)
Spago
(acoustic guitar music, Thu-Sun)
Troubadour
(live music, most nights)
William IV
(DJ, Fri & Sat)

North
Camino
(DJ, Fri & Sat)
Don Pepe
(singer, Fri & Sat)
Fratelli la Bufala
(opera singers every so often)
Hoxton Apprentice
(jazz, Tue)
Mestizo
(DJ, Thu-Sat)

Trojka
(Russian music, Fri & Sat)

Villa Bianca
(guitarist, Mon-Thu; pianist, Sat & Sun)

Yum Yum
(DJ, Fri)

South

The Gowlett
(DJ, Sun)

The Hartley
(live music, Tue)

La Lanterna
(live music)

The Little Bay: SW11
(opera, Thu-Sat; piano, Wed & Sun)

Meson don Felipe
(guitarist, nightly)

Le Pont de la Tour Bar & Grill
(pianist, nightly)

Rocket Riverside: SW15
(live music, Sun, summer only)

The Ship
(live music, Sun; quiz, Wed)

Tas: all south branches
(guitarist, nightly)

Thailand
(karaoke, Thu-Sat)

East

Club Mangia
(poker nights, Mon; wine tasting, monthly; quiz night, monthly)

The Drunken Monkey
(DJ, Wed-Sun)

Shanghai
(karaoke, nightly)

Smiths (Ground Floor)
(DJ, Wed-Sat)

Tas: EC1
(guitarist, Tue-Sun)

Tokyo City
(karaoke, Thu & Fri)

Yi-Ban: E16
(live music, Fri & Sat)

LATE
(OPEN TILL MIDNIGHT OR LATER AS SHOWN; MAY BE EARLIER SUNDAY)

Central

Kazan: SW1

Bar Italia (open 24 hours, Sun 3 am)

Boulevard

Café du Jardin

Cyprus Mangal (Sun-Thu midnight, Fri & Sat 1 am)

Le Deuxième

Eagle Bar Diner (Thu-Sat)

Ed's Easy Diner: both
W1 (midnight, Fri & Sat 1 am)

The Forge

Gaby's

Golden Dragon

Greig's

Harbour City (Fri & Sat midnight)

Itsu: W1 (Fri & Sat midnight)

Moti Mahal

Mr Kong (2.45 am, Sun 1.45 am)

New Mayflower (4 am)

Original Tajines

Pizza on the Park (Fri & Sat midnight)

Ranoush: SW1

St Alban

Satsuma (Fri & Sat midnight)

Sitaaray (1 am)

Stock Pot: W1

Sugar Reef (1 am)

Tokyo Diner

The Wolseley

West

Alounak: W14

Beirut Express: SW7; W2 (2 am)

Best Mangal

Blue Elephant

Brilliant (Fri & Sat midnight)

Buona Sera: all branches

Chelsea Bun Diner

Cochonnet (pizza till midnight)

Kandoo

Khan's of Kensington (Fri & Sat midnight)

Lowiczanka (Sat 1 am)

Mirch Masala: UB1

Mohsen

Il Pagliaccio

Ranoush: SW3; W8 (1.30 am); W2 (2.30 am)

North

Gem: N1

Ali Baba

Banners (Fri midnight)

Camino (Thu-Sat 1 am)

Gallipoli: all branches (Fri & Sat midnight)

Izgara

Kovalam (Fri & Sat midnight)

Le Mercury (1 am)

Mestizo

La Porchetta Pizzeria: *all north branches*
Vrisaki

South
Buona Sera: *all branches*
Everest Inn *(Fri & Sat midnight)*
Fujiyama
The Gowlett
Green & Blue *(Fri & Sat midnight)*
Mirch Masala: *all south branches*
Nazmins Balti House
Sree Krishna *(Fri & Sat midnight)*
Vijaya Krishna *(Fri & Sat midnight)*
Zero Degrees

East
Brick Lane Beigel Bake *(24 hours)*
Clifton *(midnight, Sat & Sun 1am)*
The Gaylord
Itsu: *E14 (Fri & Sat midnight)*
Lahore Kebab House
Mangal Ocakbasi
La Porchetta Pizzeria: *EC1*

OUTSIDE TABLES
(* PARTICULARLY RECOMMENDED)

Central
Kazan: *SW1*
Cha Cha Moon: *W1*
Apostrophe: *Barrett St W1, WC2*
Back to Basics
Bar Italia
Barrafina
Bistro 1: *Frith St W1, WC2*
Boulevard
Busaba Eathai: *WC1*
Café des Amis
Café du Jardin
Café Emm
Chisou
Ciao Bella
Dehesa
Delfino
Ed's Easy Diner: *Moor St W1*
Flat White
Galvin Bistrot de Luxe
Golden Hind
Gordon's Wine Bar*
Greig's

Hellenik
Jenny Lo's Tea House
Just Falafs: *all branches*
Leon: *Gt Marlborough St W1, WC2*
The Little Square
Mildred's
The Norfolk Arms
Original Tajines
El Pirata
Pizza on the Park
Pure California: *Goodge St W1*
Running Horse
Salt Yard
Sapori
Seafresh
Shampers
Siam Central
Soho Japan
Stock Pot: *W1*
Taro: *Brewer St W1*
La Trouvaille
Vapiano

West
Napket: *SW3*
Del'Aziz: *SW6*
Byron: *W8*
Al-Waha
The Anglesea Arms
The Atlas*
Bedlington Café
Best Mangal
La Bouchée
Café Laville
Chelsea Bun Diner
Cochonnet
Costa's Grill
Crussh: *W12*
Cumberland Arms
De Cecco*
La Delizia Limbara
Durbar
Eco: *all branches*
Il Falconiere
Gail's Bread: *all branches*
Glaisters
Gourmet Burger Kitchen: *SW6, W4*
Ground
High Road Brasserie
Indian Zing

Providores (Tapa Room) *(40)*
Rasa Samudra: *Charlotte St W1 (10,50); Dering St W1 (60)*
Rocket: *W1 (10,25)*
Royal China: *W1 (12,12,12)*
Running Horse *(35)*
Shampers *(45)*
Sitaaray *(60)*
Soho Japan *(12)*
Star Café *(30)*
Sugar Reef *(20)*
Thai Café *(22)*
La Trouvaille *(30)*
Vincent Rooms *(35)*
Yming *(12,18)*

West
Del'Aziz: *SW6 (50)*
Abu Zaad *(35)*
Adams Café *(24)*
Addie's Thai Café *(50)*
The Atlas *(40)*
La Bouchée *(55)*
Brilliant *(120)*
Chelsea Bun Diner *(50)*
Chez Marcelle *(40)*
Chez Patrick *(30)*
Cochonnet *(30)*
Le Colombier *(30)*
Crazy Homies *(35-40)*
Daquise *(20)*
De Cecco *(20)*
Eight Over Eight *(14)*
Il Falconiere *(20,35)*
Five Hot Chillies *(25)*
Gail's Bread: *W11 (15)*
Ground *(45)*
Haandi *(30)*
High Road Brasserie *(12)*
Kandoo *(30)*
Karma *(30,40)*
Khan's of Kensington *(12)*
Knaypa *(35)*
Little Bay: *SW6 (40)*
Lowiczanka *(40)*
Lucky Seven *(45)*
Made in Italy *(40)*
Madhu's *(35)*
Magic Wok *(30)*
Malabar *(30)*

Masala Zone: *SW5 (10)*
Memories of India *(30)*
Noor Jahan: *W2 (16)*
North China *(30)*
Okawari *(25)*
Il Pagliaccio *(60)*
Patio *(50)*
Pearl Liang *(45)*
Ognisko Polskie *(150)*
Princess Victoria *(60)*
Priory House *(40)*
The Red Pepper *(25)*
Riccardo's *(8)*
Royal China: *W2 (20,20)*
Saigon Saigon *(10)*
Satay House *(40)*
Taiwan Village *(17)*
Tawana *(50)*
The Thatched House *(70)*
Troubadour *(70,120)*
White Horse *(60)*
William IV *(100)*
Wine Factory *(30)*
Wine Gallery *(18,20,45)*
Wódka *(30)*

North
Gem: *N1 (100)*
Alisan *(12)*
The Almeida *(18)*
Beyoglu *(25)*
Chutneys *(60,35)*
Daphne *(50)*
Diwana Bhel-Poori House *(35)*
Fratelli la Bufala *(15,20)*
Frederick's *(18,32)*
Furnace *(30)*
Gallipoli: *Upper St N1 (50)*
Geeta *(45)*
Good Earth: *NW7 (30)*
Gung-Ho *(24)*
Hamburger Union: *N1 (20)*
Hoxton Apprentice *(25)*
Huong-Viet *(28)*
Kenwood (Brew House) *(120)*
The Lansdowne *(55)*
Lemonia *(40)*
Market *(12)*
Masala Zone: *N1 (20)*

Le Mercury *(50)*
Mestizo *(50)*
Natural Burger Co & Grill *(26)*
El Parador *(30)*
Phoenix Palace *(12,30)*
Rasa Travancore: *N16 (25)*
Rasa *(30)*
Seashell *(25)*
Snazz Sichuan *(10)*
Sushi-Say *(8)*
Toff's *(24)*
Villa Bianca *(40)*
Vrisaki *(15)*
Yelo: *N1 (35)*
Yum Yum *(100)*

South
Amaranth *(25)*
Arancia *(8)*
Brula *(24,10,10)*
La Buvette *(65)*
Chakalaka *(60)*
Chez Lindsay *(36)*
Dalchini *(40)*
Dragon Castle *(60)*
The Duke's Head *(50)*
Everest Inn *(12,25)*
Fish in a Tie *(40,20,60)*
Fujiyama *(40,25)*
The Hartley *(70)*
La Lanterna *(50,85)*
The Little Bay: *SW11 (40)*
Lola Rojo *(20)*
Ma Cuisine: *TW1 (30)*
Nazmins Balti House *(80)*
The Palmerston *(32)*
Peninsular *(100)*
Le Pont de la Tour Bar & Grill *(20)*
Ratchada *(16)*
Rocket Riverside: *SW15 (28)*
The Rye *(36)*
The Ship *(18)*
Sree Krishna *(50,60)*
Tentazioni *(25)*
Thailand *(40)*
Village East *(18)*
Zero Degrees *(35)*

East
Alba *(50)*

Clifton *(160)*
Club Mangia *(80)*
The Drunken Monkey *(10,30)*
El Faro *(60)*
Faulkner's *(18)*
Fish Central *(60)*
The Fox *(10-12)*
Moro *(14)*
New Tayyabs *(40)*
Rocket : *EC2 (25)*
Royal China: *E14 (12,12,12)*
St John *(18)*
Shanghai *(45,50)*
Smiths (Ground Floor) *(24,12,10)*
Tajima Tei *(16,6,5)*
Tas: *EC1 (50)*
Yi-Ban: *E16 (30)*

CUISINES

AMERICAN

Ⓐ★
Lucky Seven (W2)

-
Pure California (EC4, W1, WC1)

BRITISH, MODERN

Ⓐ★★
Hilliard (EC4)

★★
The Anglesea Arms (W6)
Arbutus (W1)
Arch One (SE1)
Fish Hook (W4)

Ⓐ★
Café du Jardin (WC2)
The Cow (W2)
The Fox (EC2)
Frederick's (N1)
High Road Brasserie (W4)
The Lansdowne (NW1)
The Normanby (SW15)

★
Balfour (WC1)
Bradley's (NW3)
Le Deuxième (WC2)
The Giaconda Dining
   Room (WC2)
The Hartley (SE1)
The Little Square (W1)
Market (NW1)
The Palmerston (SE22)
Phoenix Bar & Grill (SW15)
Tom Ilic (SW8)
Whits (W8)

Ⓐ-
Charles Lamb (N1)
Club Mangia (EC4)
The Duke's Head (SW15)
Queen's Head (W6)
Shampers (W1)
Smiths (Ground
   Floor) (EC1)
Tom's Deli (W11)
The Wolseley (W1)

-
Ambassador (EC1)
The Barnsbury (N1)
Café Emm (W1)

Running Horse (W1)
The Table (SE1)
Vincent Rooms (SW1)
White Horse (SW6)

BRITISH, TRADITIONAL

★★
The Anchor & Hope (SE1)
Bull and Last (NW5)
Fuzzy's Grub (EC2, EC3, EC4,
   SW1)
St John Bread & Wine (E1)

Ⓐ★
Butlers Wharf Chop
   House (SE1)

★
Greig's (W1)
Princess Victoria (W12)
The Quality Chop
   House (EC1)
St John (EC1)

Ⓐ-
Kenwood (Brew
   House) (NW3)
The Rye (SE15)
Simpson's Tavern (EC3)
Sweetings (EC4)
The Windsor Castle (W8)

-
Cock Tavern (EC1)
Kensington Square
   Kitchen (W8)
Square Pie Company (E1,
   E14, WC1)

CZECH

-
The Czechoslovak
   Restaurant (NW6)

EAST & CENT. EUROPEAN

Ⓐ-
Café Mozart (N6)
The Wolseley (W1)

-
Kipferl (EC1)
Trojka (NW1)

FISH & SEAFOOD

★★

Back to Basics *(W1)*
Chez Liline *(N4)*
Fish Club *(SW11)*
Fish Hook *(W4)*
Mandarin Kitchen *(W2)*

Ⓐ★

The Cow *(W2)*
Le Pont de la Tour Bar & Grill *(SE1)*

★

Bradley's *(NW3)*
Chez Patrick *(W8)*
Fish Central *(EC1)*
Nautilus *(NW6)*
Olympus Fish *(N3)*
Toff's *(N10)*

Ⓐ-

La Brocca *(NW6)*
Sweetings *(EC4)*

FRENCH

Ⓐ★★

Galvin at Windows *(W1)*
Galvin Bistrot de Luxe *(W1)*

★★

Ma Cuisine *(SW13, TW1, TW9)*
The Passage Café *(EC1)*

Ⓐ★

Brompton Bar & Grill *(SW3)*
Le Cercle *(SW1)*
Chez Lindsay *(TW10)*
Clos Maggiore *(WC2)*
Le Colombier *(SW3)*
Mon Plaisir *(WC2)*
La Trouvaille *(W1)*

★

The Almeida *(N1)*
Bradley's *(NW3)*
Brula *(TW1)*
La Buvette *(TW9)*
Chez Patrick *(W8)*
Whits *(W8)*

Ⓐ-

La Bouchée *(SW7)*

La Cage Imaginaire *(NW3)*
Charles Lamb *(N1)*
Le Mercury *(N1)*
Le Sacré-Coeur *(N1)*
Tartine *(SW3)*
Trinity Stores *(SW12)*

-

Café des Amis *(WC2)*
Rôtisserie Jules *(W11)*
Somerstown Coffee House *(NW1)*

FUSION

Ⓐ★

Providores (Tapa Room) *(W1)*
Village East *(SE1)*

GREEK

Ⓐ★

Hellenik *(W1)*

★

Vrisaki *(N22)*

Ⓐ-

Lemonia *(NW1)*

-

Costa's Grill *(W8)*
Daphne *(NW1)*
Kolossi Grill *(EC1)*

INTERNATIONAL

★★

Terroirs *(WC2)*

★

Govinda's *(W1)*
Mona Lisa *(SW10)*

Ⓐ-

Café Laville *(W2)*
Club Mangia *(EC4)*
Cork & Bottle *(WC2)*
The Forge *(WC2)*
Glaisters *(SW10)*
Gordon's Wine Bar *(WC2)*
Green & Blue *(SE22)*
Petek *(N4)*
Tate Modern (Level 7) *(SE1)*
The Rye *(SE15)*

The Ship (SW18)
The Thatched House (W6)
The Windsor Castle (W8)
Wine Gallery (SW10)

-

Banners (N8)
Bedford & Strand (WC2)
Boulevard (WC2)
Café in the Crypt (WC2)
Chelsea Bun Diner (SW10)
The Deptford Project (SE8)
Hoxton Apprentice (N1)
Putney Station (SW15)
Star Café (W1)
Stock Pot (SW1, SW3, W1)
Sugar Reef (W1)
Wine Factory (W11)

ITALIAN

Ⓐ★★

Bocca Di Lupo (W1)
Dehesa (W1)
Philpotts Mezzaluna (NW2)
Pizza Metro (SW11)

★★

Salt Yard (W1)
Tentazioni (SE1)

Ⓐ★

Aglio e Olio (SW10)
Il Bordello (E1)
Caffè Vergnano (WC2)
Ciao Bella (WC1)
Frantoio (SW10)
Mediterraneo (W11)
Osteria Basilico (W11)
Pappa Ciccia (SW15, SW6)
Princi (W1)
Spacca Napoli (W1)

★

Alba (EC1)
La Delizia Limbara (SW3)
Fratelli la Bufala (NW3)
La Lanterna (SE1)
Oliveto (SW1)
Paolina Café (WC1)
Pizzeria Oregano (N1)
Le Querce (SE23)
The Red Pepper (W9)
Spago (SW7)
Stringray Globe Café (E2)

Ⓐ-

Arancia (SE16)
La Brocca (NW6)
Buona Sera (SW11, SW3)
Il Pagliaccio (SW6)
E Pellicci (E2)
Pizza on the Park (SW1)
Riccardo's (SW3)
Trinity Stores (SW12)

-

Amato (W1)
L'Artista (NW11)
Bar Trattoria
  Semplice (W1)
Da Mario (SW7)
De Cecco (SW6)
Delfino (W1)
Esca (SW4)
Il Falconiere (SW7)
Made in Italy (SW3)
Marine Ices (NW3)
La Porchetta Pizzeria (EC1,
  N1, N4, NW1, WC1)
Sapori (WC2)
Vapiano (W1)
Villa Bianca (NW3)

MEDITERRANEAN

★★

Salt Yard (W1)

Ⓐ★

The Atlas (SW6)
Mediterraneo (W11)
St Alban (SW1)
William IV (NW10)

★

Cochonnet (W9)
The Eagle (EC1)
Hummus Bros (W1, WC1)
Mem & Laz (N1)

Ⓐ-

Del'Aziz (NW3, SE1, SW6, W12)
Fish in a Tie (SW11)
The Little Bay (EC1, NW6,
  SW11, SW6)
The Norfolk Arms (WC1)
Petek (N4)
Rocket (W1)
Rocket (EC2)
Rocket Riverside (SW15)
Tom's Deli (W11)

Troubadour *(SW5)*

-
Ambassador *(EC1)*
Bistro 1 *(W1, WC2)*
Cumberland Arms *(W14)*
Made in Italy *(SW3)*
Priory House *(W14)*

ORGANIC

🅐★
Story Deli *(E1)*

★
The Hartley *(SE1)*

POLISH

★
Knaypa *(W6)*

🅐-
Ognisko Polskie *(SW7)*
Patio *(W12)*

-
Daquise *(SW7)*
Lowiczanka *(W6)*
Wódka *(W8)*

PORTUGUESE

★★
Lisboa Pâtisserie *(W10)*

RUSSIAN

-
Potemkin *(EC1)*
Trojka *(NW1)*

SCANDINAVIAN

🅐-
Nordic Bakery *(W1)*

SPANISH

🅐★★
Barrafina *(W1)*
Dehesa *(W1)*
Moro *(EC1)*

★★
El Faro *(E14)*
Salt Yard *(W1)*

🅐★
Lola Rojo *(SW11)*
Rebato's *(SW8)*

★
Casa Brindisa *(SW7)*
Navarro's *(W1)*
Pinchito *(EC1)*

🅐-
don Fernando's *(TW9)*
Don Pepe *(NW8)*
Meson don Felipe *(SE1)*
The Norfolk Arms *(WC1)*
El Rincón Latino *(SW4)*

-
Camino *(N1)*
Galicia *(W10)*
Los Molinos *(W6)*
El Parador *(NW1)*
El Pirata *(W1)*
Tapas Brindisa *(SE1)*

STEAKS & GRILLS

🅐★
Le Pont de la Tour Bar &
   Grill *(SE1)*

★
Haché *(NW1, SW10)*

🅐-
Simpson's Tavern *(EC3)*
Smiths (Ground
   Floor) *(EC1)*

-
Popeseye *(SW15, W14)*
Rôtisserie Jules *(SW7)*

VEGETARIAN

★★
Geeta *(NW6)*
Jashan *(HA0)*
Kastoori *(SW17)*
Rasa *(N16)*
Rasa Maricham *(WC1)*
Rasa Samudra *(W1)*
Rasa Travancore *(N16)*
Sagar *(TW1, W1, W6)*
Sree Krishna *(SW17)*
Vijay *(NW6)*

A★
Blue Elephant (SW6)
Ganapati (SE15)
Malabar Junction (WC1)
The Place Below (EC2)

★
Carnevale (EC1)
Chutneys (NW1)
Diwana Bhel-Poori House (NW1)
Food for Thought (WC2)
Govinda's (W1)
Kovalam (NW6)
Ragam (W1)
Rani (N3)
Sakonis (HA0)

–
India Club (WC2)
Masala Zone (N1, SW5, W1, W2)
Mildred's (W1)
Woodlands (NW3, SW1, W1)
World Food Café (WC2)

AFTERNOON TEA

★★
Yauatcha (W1)

A–
Napket (SW3, W1)
The Wolseley (W1)

–
Daquise (SW7)

BURGERS, ETC

A★
Ground (W4)
Lucky Seven (W2)

★
Gourmet Burger Kitchen (EC4, NW3, SW11, SW15, SW4, SW5, SW6, SW7, W1, W11, W2, W4, WC2)
Haché (NW1, SW10)
Hamburger Union (N1, W1, WC2)
Natural Burger Co & Grill (NW8)

A–
Byron (W12, W8)
Eagle Bar Diner (W1)
Ed's Easy Diner (W1, WC2)

CREPES

A★
Chez Lindsay (TW10)

FISH & CHIPS

★★
Faulkner's (E8)
Fish Club (SW11)
Golden Hind (W1)

★
Brady's (SW18)
Costa's Fish Restaurant (W8)
Fryer's Delight (WC1)
Masters Super Fish (SE1)
Nautilus (NW6)
North Sea Fish (WC1)
Olley's (SE24)
Rock & Sole Plaice (WC2)
Seashell (NW1)
Toff's (N10)
Two Brothers (N3)

–
The Sea Cow (SE22)
Seafresh (SW1)

ICE CREAM

A★
Albion (E2)

–
Marine Ices (NW3)

PIZZA

A★★
Pizza Metro (SW11)

★★
Franco Manca (SW9)

A★
Il Bordello (E1)
The Gowlett (SE15)
Osteria Basilico (W11)
Story Deli (E1)

★
Cochonnet (W9)
La Delizia Limbara (SW3)
Eco (SW4, W4)
Furnace (N1)

La Lanterna *(SE1)*
Oliveto *(SW1)*
Pizzeria Oregano *(N1)*
Spago *(SW7)*

A-
Buona Sera *(SW11, SW3)*
Pizza on the Park *(SW1)*
Rocket *(W1)*
Rocket *(EC2)*
Rocket Riverside *(SW15)*
Zero Degrees *(SE3)*

-
Da Mario *(SW7)*
Delfino *(W1)*
Made in Italy *(SW3)*
Marine Ices *(NW3)*
La Porchetta Pizzeria *(EC1, N1, N4, NW1, WC1)*
Sapori *(WC2)*

SANDWICHES, CAKES, ETC

A★★
Monmouth Coffee
  Company *(SE1, WC2)*

★★
Brick Lane Beigel
  Bake *(E1)*
Fuzzy's Grub *(EC2, EC3, EC4, SE1, SW1)*
Lisboa Pâtisserie *(W10)*

A★
Caffé Vergnano *(SE1)*
Maison Bertaux *(W1)*

★
Amano *(SE1)*
Apostrophe *(EC2, EC4, SW1, W1, WC2)*
Fernandez & Wells *(W1)*
Flat White *(W1)*
La Fromagerie Café *(W1)*
Gail's Bread *(NW3, W11)*
Just Falafs *(W1, WC2)*
Konditor & Cook *(EC3, W1, WC1)*
Paul *(EC4, NW3, SW7, W1, WC2)*
Spianata & Co *(E1, EC1, EC2, EC3, EC4)*

A-
Bar Italia *(W1)*
Kenwood (Brew
  House) *(NW3)*
Napket *(SW3, W1)*

Tom's Deli *(W11)*
Troubadour *(SW5)*

-
Amato *(W1)*
Boiled Egg &
  Soldiers *(SW11)*
Chamomile *(NW3)*
Crussh *(E14, EC3, EC4, W1, W12, W8)*
Le Pain Quotidien *(SW7)*
Leon *(E1, E14, EC4, SE1, SW3, W1, WC2)*
Le Pain Quotidien *(NW1, SE1, SW3, W1, W8)*
Salade *(EC4, W1, W2)*

SALADS

★★
Beirut Express *(SW7, W2)*

★
Chop'd *(E1, E14, EC3, NW1, W1)*
Just Falafs *(W1, WC2)*

-
Le Pain Quotidien *(WC1)*
Pure California *(W1, WC1)*
Salade *(EC4, W1, W2)*

BRAZILIAN

-
Preto *(SW1)*

MEXICAN/TEXMEX

A★
Crazy Homies *(W2)*

★
Mestizo *(NW1)*
Santo *(W10)*

A-
Taqueria *(W11)*
Wahaca *(W12, WC2)*

SOUTH AMERICAN

★★
El Vergel *(SE1)*

★
Sabor *(N1)*

MOROCCAN

𝔸★
Adams Café (W12)

-
Original Tajines (W1)

NORTH AFRICAN

𝔸-
Del'Aziz (SW6)

-
Azou (W6)

SOUTH AFRICAN

★
Chakalaka (SW15)

TUNISIAN

𝔸★
Adams Café (W12)

EGYPTIAN

★
Ali Baba (NW1)

ISRAELI

-
Gaby's (WC2)

LEBANESE

★★
Beirut Express (SW7, W2)
Chez Marcelle (W14)

★
Fresco (W2)

-
Al-Waha (W2)
Ranoush (SW1, SW3, W2, W8)

MIDDLE EASTERN

-
Esca (SW4)
Patogh (W1)

PERSIAN

★★
Mohsen (W14)

★
Alounak (W14, W2)
Kandoo (W2)

SYRIAN

𝔸★
Abu Zaad (W12)

TURKISH

★★
Mangal Ocakbasi (E8)

𝔸★
Best Mangal (W14)
Gem (N1, SW4)

★
Beyoglu (NW3)
Cyprus Mangal (SW1)

𝔸-
Gallipoli (N1)
Petek (N4)
Tas (EC1, SE1, WC1)

-
Haz (E1, EC3)
Izgara (N3)
Kazan (EC3, SW1)

AFGHANI

★
Afghan Kitchen (N1)

BURMESE

★★
Mandalay (W2)

CHINESE

𝔸★★
Min Jiang (W8)

★★
Alisan (HA9)
Jenny Lo's Tea House (SW1)
Mandarin Kitchen (W2)
Taiwan Village (SW6)

Yauatcha (W1)
Yming (W1)

𝔸★

Dalchini (SW19)
Good Earth (NW7, SW3)
Pearl Liang (W2)
Shanghai (E8)
Snazz Sichuan (NW1)

★

China Boulevard (SW18)
The Four Seasons (W2)
Gung-Ho (NW6)
Joy King Lau (WC2)
Magic Wok (W2)
Mr Kong (WC2)
New Mayflower (W1)
North China (W3)
Peninsular (SE10)
Phoenix Palace (NW1)
Royal China (E14, W1, W2)
Royal China (SW6)
Sakonis (HA0)
Singapore Garden (NW6)
Stick & Bowl (W8)
Yi-Ban (E16, SW6)

𝔸-

The Drunken Monkey (E1)

-

The Chinese
   Experience (W1)
Chuen Cheng Ku (W1)
Dragon Castle (SE17)
Golden Dragon (W1)
Harbour City (W1)
New World (W1)
O'Zon (TW1)
Wong Kei (W1)

CHINESE, DIM SUM

★★

Alisan (HA9)
Yauatcha (W1)

𝔸★

Pearl Liang (W2)
Shanghai (E8)

★

China Boulevard (SW18)
Joy King Lau (WC2)
Phoenix Palace (NW1)
Royal China (E14, W1, W2)

Royal China (SW6)
Yi-Ban (E16, SW6)

𝔸-

Cha Cha Moon (W1, W2)
The Drunken Monkey (E1)
The Electric
   Birdcage (SW1)

-

The Chinese
   Experience (W1)
Chuen Cheng Ku (W1)
Dragon Castle (SE17)
Golden Dragon (W1)
Harbour City (W1)
New World (W1)

INDIAN

𝔸★★

Babur Brasserie (SE23)
Hot Stuff (SW8)
Indian Zing (W6)

★★

Geeta (NW6)
Jashan (HA0)
Kastoori (SW17)
Lovage (SE1)
Madhu's (UB1)
Mango & Silk (SW14)
Mirch Masala (E1, SW16, SW17,
   UB1, W14)
New Tayyabs (E1)
Sagar (TW1, W1, W6)
Sree Krishna (SW17)
Vijay (NW6)

𝔸★

Bangalore Express (SE1)
Dalchini (SW19)
Ganapati (SE15)
Malabar (W8)
Malabar Junction (WC1)
Moti Mahal (WC2)
Nanglo (SW12)
Sitaaray (WC2)
Tandoori Nights (SE22)

★

Brilliant (UB2)
Chowki (W1)
Chutney (SW18)
Chutneys (NW1)
Clifton (E1)

Diwana Bhel-Poori House (NW1)
Eriki (NW3)
Five Hot Chillies (HA0)
Great Nepalese (NW1)
Haandi (SW3)
Imli (W1)
Indian Ocean (SW17)
Karma (W14)
Khan's (W2)
Khan's of Kensington (SW7)
Kovalam (NW6)
Ma Goa (SW15)
Mango Tree (SE1)
Mela (SE24, WC2)
Memsaheb on Thames (E14)
Nazmins Balti House (SW18)
Noor Jahan (SW5, W2)
Ragam (W1)
Rani (N3)
Red Fort (W1)
Sakonis (HA0, SW17)
Tangawizi (TW1)

-

Durbar (W2)
Everest Inn (SE3)
The Gaylord (E14)
Gopal's of Soho (W1)
India Club (WC2)
Kasturi (EC3)
Masala Zone (N1, SW5, W1, W2)
Memories of India (SW7)
Rooburoo (N1)
Shikara (SW3)
Woodlands (NW3, SW1, W1)

INDIAN, SOUTHERN

★★
Geeta (NW6)
Jashan (HA0)
Kastoori (SW17)
Rasa (N16)
Rasa Maricham (WC1)
Rasa Samudra (W1)
Rasa Travancore (N16)
Sagar (TW1, W1, W6)
Sree Krishna (SW17)
Vijay (NW6)

𝔸★
Ganapati (SE15)

Malabar Junction (WC1)

★
Chutneys (NW1)
Kovalam (NW6)
Ragam (W1)
Rani (N3)
Shilpa (W6)

-

India Club (WC2)
Vijaya Krishna (SW17)
Woodlands (NW3, SW1, W1)

JAPANESE

𝔸★★
Edokko (WC1)

★★
Dinings (W1)
Inaho (W2)
Jin Kichi (NW3)
Pham Sushi (EC1)
Tosa (W6)

𝔸★
Abeno (WC1)
Centrepoint Sushi (WC2)

★
Abokado (WC2)
Café Japan (NW11)
Chisou (W1)
Hazuki (WC2)
Itsu (E14, SW3, W1)
K10 (EC2)
Kulu Kulu (W1)
Kurumaya (EC4)
Misato (W1)
Mitsukoshi (SW1)
Okawari (W5)
Sakura (W1)
Satsuma (W1)
Sushi-Say (NW2)
Tajima Tei (EC1)
Ten Ten Tei (W1)
Tokyo City (EC2)
Yoshino (W1)
Yuzu (NW6)

𝔸-
Inamo (W1)

-

Bento (NW1)
Fujiyama (SW9)

Inshoku *(SE1)*
Soho Japan *(W1)*
Taro *(W1)*
Tokyo Diner *(WC2)*

KOREAN

𝔸★★
Koba *(W1)*

★
Woo Jung *(WC2)*

MALAYSIAN

★
C&R Cafe *(W1)*
Ekachai *(EC2, SW18)*
54 Farringdon Road *(EC1)*
Satay House *(W2)*
Singapore Garden *(NW6)*

-
Café de Maya *(NW8)*
Nyonya *(W11)*

PAKISTANI

★★
Lahore Kebab House *(E1)*
Mirch Masala *(E1, SW16, SW17, UB1)*
New Tayyabs *(E1)*

PAN-ASIAN

𝔸★
Eight Over Eight *(SW3)*
Uli *(W11)*

★
Haozhan *(W1)*
Hare & Tortoise *(SW15, SW5, W14, WC1)*

𝔸-
Chi Noodle & Wine Bar *(EC4)*
The Electric Birdcage *(SW1)*

-
The Banana Leaf Canteen *(SW11)*
O'Zon *(TW1)*
Tampopo *(SW10)*

THAI

𝔸★★
Amaranth *(SW18)*

★★
Esarn Kheaw *(W12)*
The Paddyfield *(SW12)*
Patara *(SW3, W1)*

𝔸★
Addie's Thai Café *(SW5)*
Blue Elephant *(SW6)*
Churchill Arms *(W8)*
Yum Yum *(N16)*

★
Bangkok *(SW7)*
C&R Cafe *(W1)*
Ekachai *(EC2, SW18)*
Hammersmith Café *(W6)*
Latymers *(W6)*
Talad Thai *(SW15)*
Tawana *(W2)*
Thai Corner Café *(SE22)*
Tong Ka Nom Thai *(NW10)*

𝔸-
Busaba Eathai *(W1, WC1)*
Café 209 *(SW6)*
The Pepper Tree *(SW4)*
The Rye *(SE15)*
The Walmer Castle *(W11)*

-
Bedlington Café *(W4)*
Blue Jade *(SW1)*
Café de Maya *(NW8)*
Old Parr's Head *(W14)*
Ratchada *(SE3)*
Rosa's *(E1)*
Siam Central *(W1)*
Thai Café *(SW1)*
Thai Garden *(SW11)*
Thailand *(SE14)*
Yelo *(N1)*
Yelo Thai Canteen *(W11)*

VIETNAMESE

★★
The Paddyfield *(SW12)*
Sông Quê *(E2)*

𝔸★
Namo *(E9)*
Pho *(EC1, W1)*

★
Cây Tre *(EC1)*
Huong-Viet *(N1)*
Khoai *(N8)*
Khoai Cafe *(N12)*
Viet *(W1)*

-
Saigon Saigon *(W6)*
Viet Garden *(N1)*

AREA OVERVIEWS

Where the ratings for a restaurant appear in brackets, eg (𝔸★), you can usually keep expenditure within our £25-a-head budget only at certain times of the day, or by sticking to a particular menu. Eating at other times or from the à la carte menu may be much more expensive.

CENTRAL

Soho, Covent Garden & Bloomsbury
(Parts of W1, all WC2 and WC1)

£25	Arbutus	*British, Modern*	(★★)
	The Giaconda	*"*	(★)
	Clos Maggiore	*French*	(𝔸★)
	Sitaaray	*Indian*	(𝔸★)
£20+	Café du Jardin	*British, Modern*	(𝔸★)
	Balfour	*"*	★
	Le Deuxième	*"*	(★)
	Shampers	*"*	(𝔸)
	La Trouvaille	*French*	(𝔸★)
	Café des Amis	*"*	-
	Terroirs	*International*	(★★)
	Cork & Bottle	*"*	𝔸
	The Forge	*"*	(𝔸)
	Bedford & Strand	*"*	-
	Boulevard	*"*	-
	Dehesa	*Italian*	𝔸★★
	Bocca Di Lupo	*"*	(𝔸★★)
	Ciao Bella	*"*	𝔸★
	Spacca Napoli	*"*	𝔸★
	Sapori	*"*	-
	Barrafina	*Spanish*	(𝔸★★)
	Mildred's	*Vegetarian*	-
	Yauatcha	*Chinese*	(★★)
	Golden Dragon	*"*	-
	Malabar Junction	*Indian*	𝔸★
	Moti Mahal	*"*	(𝔸★)
	Chowki	*"*	★
	Red Fort	*"*	(★)
	Edokko	*Japanese*	𝔸★★
	Abeno	*"*	𝔸★
	Ten Ten Tei	*"*	★
	Inamo	*"*	𝔸
	Haozhan	*Pan-Asian*	★
	Patara	*Thai*	(★★)
£15+	Café Emm	*British, Modern*	-
	Mon Plaisir	*French*	(𝔸★)
	Gordon's Wine Bar	*International*	𝔸
	Café in the Crypt	*"*	-
	Star Café	*"*	-
	Sugar Reef	*"*	-
	Caffè Vergnano	*Italian*	𝔸★
	Paolina Café	*"*	★
	Amato	*"*	-
	La Porchetta Pizzeria	*"*	-
	The Norfolk Arms	*Mediterranean*	𝔸
	Bistro 1	*"*	-
	World Food Café	*Vegetarian*	-
	Gourmet Burger Kitchen	*Burgers, etc*	★
	Ed's Easy Diner	*"*	𝔸
	North Sea Fish	*Fish & chips*	★

	Rock & Sole Plaice	"	★
	Paul	Sandwiches, cakes, etc	★
	Le Pain Quotidien	"	-
	Le Pain Quotidien	Salads	-
	Wahaca	Mexican/TexMex	𝔸
	Tas	Turkish	𝔸
	Yming	Chinese	(★★)
	Joy King Lau	"	★
	Mr Kong	"	★
	New Mayflower	"	★
	The Chinese Experience	"	-
	Chuen Cheng Ku	"	-
	Harbour City	"	-
	New World	"	-
	Cha Cha Moon	Chinese, Dim sum	𝔸
	Imli	Indian	★
	Mela	"	(★)
	Gopal's of Soho	"	-
	India Club	"	-
	Masala Zone	"	-
	Rasa Maricham	Indian, Southern	★★
	Centrepoint Sushi	Japanese	𝔸★
	Itsu	"	★
	Kulu Kulu	"	★
	Satsuma	"	★
	Hazuki	"	(★)
	Taro	"	-
	Tokyo Diner	"	-
	Hare & Tortoise	Pan-Asian	★
	C&R Cafe	Thai	★
£10+	Pure California	American	-
	Square Pie Company	British, Traditional	-
	Stock Pot	International	-
	Princi	Italian	𝔸★
	Hummus Bros	Mediterranean	★
	Nordic Bakery	Scandinavian	𝔸
	Food for Thought	Vegetarian	★
	Napket	Afternoon tea	𝔸
	Hamburger Union	Burgers, etc	★
	Fernandez & Wells	Sandwiches, cakes, etc	★
	Bar Italia	"	𝔸
	Leon	"	-
	Just Falafs	Salads	★
	Gaby's	Israeli	-
	Wong Kei	Chinese	-
	Abokado	Japanese	★
	Misato	"	★
	Busaba Eathai	Thai	𝔸
	Viet	Vietnamese	★
£5+	Fryer's Delight	Fish & chips	★
	Monmouth Coffee Co	Sandwiches, cakes, etc	𝔸★★
	Maison Bertaux	"	𝔸★
	Apostrophe	"	★
	Flat White	"	★
	Konditor & Cook	"	★

Mayfair & St James's (Parts of W1 and SW1)

£25	Galvin at Windows	*French*	(Ⓐ★★)
	St Alban	*Mediterranean*	(Ⓐ★)
£20+	Running Horse	*British, Modern*	-
	Rocket	*Mediterranean*	(Ⓐ)
	Delfino	*Pizza*	-
	Chisou	*Japanese*	★
	Mitsukoshi	*"*	(★)
	Patara	*Thai*	(★★)
£15+	The Little Square	*British, Modern*	★
	The Wolseley	*"*	(Ⓐ)
	Greig's	*British, Traditional*	(★)
	Bar Trattoria Semplice	*Italian*	-
	El Pirata	*Spanish*	-
	Woodlands	*Indian*	-
	Rasa	*Indian, Southern*	★★
	Sakura	*Japanese*	★
	Yoshino	*"*	(★)
	The Electric Birdcage	*Pan-Asian*	Ⓐ
£10+	Stock Pot	*International*	-
	Napket	*Afternoon tea*	Ⓐ
	Fuzzy's Grub	*Sandwiches, cakes, etc*	★★
	Crussh	*"*	-
	Chop'd	*Salads*	★
	Salade	*"*	-
	Busaba Eathai	*Thai*	Ⓐ
£5+	Apostrophe	*Sandwiches, cakes, etc*	★

Fitzrovia & Marylebone (Part of W1)

£25	Galvin Bistrot de Luxe	*French*	(Ⓐ★★)
£20+	Providores (Tapa Room)	*Fusion*	(Ⓐ★)
	Hellenik	*Greek*	Ⓐ★
	Salt Yard	*Mediterranean*	★★
	Navarro's	*Spanish*	★
	Royal China	*Chinese*	(★)
	Soho Japan	*Japanese*	-
	Koba	*Korean*	(Ⓐ★★)
£15+	Back to Basics	*Fish & seafood*	(★★)
	Vapiano	*Italian*	-
	Eagle Bar Diner	*Burgers, etc*	Ⓐ
	La Fromagerie Café	*Sandwiches, cakes, etc*	★
	Paul	*"*	★
	Le Pain Quotidien	*"*	-
	Original Tajines	*Moroccan*	-
	Patogh	*Middle Eastern*	-
	Ragam	*Indian*	★
	Woodlands	*"*	-
	Rasa Samudra	*Indian, Southern*	★★
	Dinings	*Japanese*	(★★)
	Woo Jung	*Korean*	★

£10+	Pure California	American	-
	Govinda's	International	★
	Hamburger Union	Burgers, etc	★
	Golden Hind	Fish & chips	★★
	Leon	Sandwiches, cakes, etc	-
	Sagar	Indian	★★
	Siam Central	Thai	-
	Pho	Vietnamese	𝔸★
£5+	Apostrophe	Sandwiches, cakes, etc	★

Belgravia, Pimlico, Victoria & Westminster (SW1, except St James's)

£25	Oliveto	Pizza	(★)
£20+	Le Cercle	French	𝔸★
	Pizza on the Park	Italian	𝔸
	Preto	Brazilian	-
£15+	Vincent Rooms	British, Modern	-
	Seafresh	Fish & chips	-
	Cyprus Mangal	Turkish	★
	Kazan	"	-
	Blue Jade	Thai	-
	Thai Café	"	-
£10+	Ranoush	Lebanese	-
	Jenny Lo's	Chinese	★★
£5+	Apostrophe	Sandwiches, cakes, etc	★

WEST

Chelsea, South Kensington, Kensington, Earl's Court & Fulham (SW3, SW5, SW6, SW7, SW10 & W8)

£20+	Whits	British, Modern	(★)
	Chez Patrick	Fish & seafood	(★)
	Brompton Bar & Grill	French	(A★)
	Le Colombier	"	(A★)
	Tartine	"	A
	La Bouchée	"	(A)
	Glaisters	International	A
	Wine Gallery	"	A
	Aglio e Olio	Italian	A★
	Frantoio	"	(A★)
	Buona Sera	"	A
	Il Pagliaccio	"	A
	Riccardo's	"	A
	Da Mario	"	-
	Made in Italy	"	-
	De Cecco	"	-
	Il Falconiere	"	-
	The Atlas	Mediterranean	A★
	Del'Aziz	"	(A)
	Wódka	Polish	-
	Casa Brindisa	Spanish	★
	Beirut Express	Lebanese	★★
	Min Jiang	Chinese	(A★★)
	Taiwan Village	"	★★
	Royal China	"	(★)
	Khan's of Kensington	Indian	★
	Noor Jahan	"	★
	Haandi	"	(★)
	Shikara	"	-
	Tampopo	Pan-Asian	-
	Patara	Thai	(★★)
	Blue Elephant	"	(A★)
	Bangkok	"	★
£15+	White Horse	British, Modern	-
	Kensington Square Kitchen	British, Traditional	-
	Costa's Grill	Greek	-
	The Windsor Castle	International	A
	Chelsea Bun Diner	"	-
	Pappa Ciccia	Italian	A★
	Spago	"	★
	Little Bay	Mediterranean	A
	Ognisko Polskie	Polish	(A)
	Daquise	"	-
	Haché	Steaks & grills	★
	Rôtisserie Jules	"	-
	Gourmet Burger Kitchen	Burgers, etc	★
	La Delizia Limbara	Pizza	★
	Paul	Sandwiches, cakes, etc	★
	Troubadour	"	A
	Le Pain Quotidien	"	-

	Good Earth	*Chinese*	*(A★)*
	Stick & Bowl	*"*	★
	Yi-Ban	*"*	*(★)*
	Malabar	*Indian*	A★
	Masala Zone	*"*	-
	Memories of India	*"*	
	Itsu	*Japanese*	★
	Eight Over Eight	*Pan-Asian*	*(A★)*
	Hare & Tortoise	*"*	★
	Addie's Thai Café	*Thai*	A★
	Churchill Arms	*"*	A★
£10+	Mona Lisa	*International*	★
	Stock Pot	*"*	-
	Napket	*Afternoon tea*	A
	Byron	*Burgers, etc*	A
	Costa's Fish	*Fish & chips*	★
	Crussh	*Sandwiches, cakes, etc*	-
	Leon	*"*	-
	Ranoush	*Lebanese*	-
	Café 209	*Thai*	A

Notting Hill, Holland Park, Bayswater, North Kensington & Maida Vale (W2, W9, W10, W11)

£25	Osteria Basilico	*Italian*	*(A★)*
	Satay House	*Malaysian*	*(★)*
£20+	The Cow	*British, Modern*	*(A★)*
	Wine Factory	*International*	-
	Mediterraneo	*Italian*	*(A★)*
	The Red Pepper	*"*	★
	Beirut Express	*Lebanese*	★★
	Al-Waha	*"*	-
	Pearl Liang	*Chinese*	*(A★)*
	The Four Seasons	*"*	★
	Royal China	*"*	*(★)*
	Noor Jahan	*Indian*	★
	The Walmer Castle	*Thai*	A
£15+	Lucky Seven	*American*	A★
	Rôtisserie Jules	*French*	-
	Café Laville	*International*	A
	Cochonnet	*Mediterranean*	★
	Galicia	*Spanish*	-
	Gourmet Burger Kitchen	*Burgers, etc*	★
	Tom's Deli	*Sandwiches, cakes, etc*	*(A)*
	Crazy Homies	*Mexican/TexMex*	A★
	Santo	*"*	*(★)*
	Taqueria	*"*	A
	Alounak	*Persian*	★
	Mandarin Kitchen	*Chinese*	*(★★)*
	Magic Wok	*"*	★
	Cha Cha Moon	*Chinese, Dim sum*	A
	Khan's	*Indian*	★
	Durbar	*"*	-
	Masala Zone	*"*	-

	Inaho	Japanese	(★★)
	Nyonya	Malaysian	-
	Uli	Pan-Asian	𝔸★
	Tawana	Thai	★
£10+	Gail's Bread	Sandwiches, cakes, etc	★
	Salade	Salads	-
	Ranoush	Lebanese	-
	Kandoo	Persian	★
	Mandalay	Burmese	★★
	Yelo Thai Canteen	Thai	-
£5+	Fresco	Lebanese	★
£1+	Lisboa Pâtisserie	Sandwiches, cakes, etc	★★

Hammersmith, Shepherd's Bush, Olympia, Chiswick & Ealing (W4, W5, W6, W12, W14)

£20+	The Anglesea Arms	British, Modern	★★
	High Road Brasserie	"	(𝔸★)
	Fish Hook	Fish & seafood	(★★)
	The Thatched House	International	𝔸
	Del'Aziz	Mediterranean	(𝔸)
	Cumberland Arms	"	-
	Priory House	"	-
	Knaypa	Polish	★
	Patio	"	(𝔸)
	Lowiczanka	"	-
	Los Molinos	Spanish	-
	Popeseye	Steaks & grills	-
	Adams Café	Moroccan	𝔸★
	Azou	North African	-
	North China	Chinese	★
	Indian Zing	Indian	𝔸★★
	Saigon Saigon	Vietnamese	-
£15+	Queen's Head	British, Modern	𝔸
	Princess Victoria	British, Traditional	(★)
	Ground	Burgers, etc	𝔸★
	Gourmet Burger Kitchen	"	★
	Eco	Pizza	★
	Wahaca	Mexican/TexMex	𝔸
	Chez Marcelle	Lebanese	★★
	Mohsen	Persian	★★
	Alounak	"	★
	Best Mangal	Turkish	𝔸★
	Madhu's	Indian	★★
	Brilliant	"	★
	Karma	"	★
	Shilpa	Indian, Southern	★
	Okawari	Japanese	★
	Hare & Tortoise	Pan-Asian	★
	Esarn Kheaw	Thai	★★
	Latymers	"	★
	Bedlington Café	"	-
	Old Parr's Head	"	-

£10+	Byron	Burgers, etc	A
	Crussh	Sandwiches, cakes, etc	-
	Abu Zaad	Syrian	A★
	Mirch Masala	Indian	★★
	Sagar	"	★★
	Tosa	Japanese	(★★)
	Hammersmith Café	Thai	★

NORTH

Hampstead, West Hampstead, St John's Wood, Regent's Park, Kilburn & Camden Town (NW postcodes)

£20+			
	The Lansdowne	*British, Modern*	(Ⓐ★)
	Bradley's	"	(★)
	Bull and Last	*British, Traditional*	★★
	La Cage Imaginaire	*French*	(Ⓐ)
	Somerstown Coffee House	"	-
	Philpotts Mezzaluna	*Italian*	(Ⓐ★★)
	La Brocca	"	Ⓐ
	Villa Bianca	"	-
	William IV	*Mediterranean*	Ⓐ★
	Del'Aziz	"	(Ⓐ)
	Don Pepe	*Spanish*	Ⓐ
	Seashell	*Fish & chips*	★
	Snazz Sichuan	*Chinese*	Ⓐ★
	Gung-Ho	"	★
	Phoenix Palace	"	★
	Eriki	*Indian*	★
	Singapore Garden	*Malaysian*	(★)
£15+			
	Market	*British, Modern*	(★)
	The Czech Restaurant	*Czech*	-
	Daphne	*Greek*	
	Fratelli la Bufala	*Italian*	(★)
	L'Artista	"	-
	Marine Ices	"	-
	La Porchetta Pizzeria	"	-
	The Little Bay	*Mediterranean*	Ⓐ
	Trojka	*Russian*	-
	El Parador	*Spanish*	-
	Haché	*Steaks & grills*	★
	Gourmet Burger Kitchen	*Burgers, etc*	★
	Paul	*Sandwiches, cakes, etc*	★
	Kenwood (Brew House)	"	Ⓐ
	Chamomile	"	-
	Le Pain Quotidien	"	-
	Mestizo	*Mexican/TexMex*	(★)
	Beyoglu	*Turkish*	★
	Alisan	*Chinese*	★★
	Good Earth	"	(Ⓐ★)
	Geeta	*Indian*	★★
	Vijay	"	★★
	Diwana B-P House	"	★
	Great Nepalese	"	★
	Kovalam	"	★
	Sakonis	"	★
	Woodlands	"	-
	Jin Kichi	*Japanese*	★★
	Café Japan	"	★
	Sushi-Say	"	★
	Yuzu	"	★
	Tong Ka Nom Thai	*Thai*	★

£10+	Lemonia	Greek	(Ⓐ)
	Natural Burger Co & Grill	Burgers, etc	★
	Nautilus	Fish & chips	★
	Gail's Bread	Sandwiches, cakes, etc	★
	Chop'd	Salads	★
	Ali Baba	Egyptian	★
	Jashan	Indian	★★
	Chutneys	"	★
	Five Hot Chillies	"	★
	Bento	Japanese	-
	Café de Maya	Thai	-

Hoxton, Islington, Highgate, Crouch End, Stoke Newington, Finsbury Park, Muswell Hill & Finchley (N postcodes)

£25	Vrisaki	Greek	(★)
£20+	Frederick's	British, Modern	(Ⓐ★)
	Charles Lamb	"	Ⓐ
	Chez Liline	Fish & seafood	(★★)
	The Almeida	French	(★)
	Banners	International	-
	Furnace	Pizza	★
	Sabor	South American	(★)
	Rani	Indian	★
£15+	The Barnsbury	British, Modern	-
	Café Mozart	East & Cent. European	Ⓐ
	Olympus Fish	Fish & seafood	★
	Le Mercury	French	Ⓐ
	Hoxton Apprentice	International	-
	Pizzeria Oregano	Italian	★
	La Porchetta Pizzeria	"	-
	Mem & Laz	Mediterranean	★
	Camino	Spanish	-
	Toff's	Fish & chips	★
	Two Brothers	"	★
	Gallipoli	Turkish	Ⓐ
	Petek	"	Ⓐ
	Afghan Kitchen	Afghani	★
	Masala Zone	Indian	-
	Rooburoo	"	-
	Rasa	Indian, Southern	★★
	Rasa Travancore	"	★★
	Yum Yum	Thai	Ⓐ★
	Viet Garden	Vietnamese	-
£10+	Le Sacré-Coeur	French	(Ⓐ)
	Hamburger Union	Burgers, etc	★
	Gem	Turkish	Ⓐ★
	Izgara	"	-
	Yelo	Thai	-
	Huong-Viet	Vietnamese	★
	Khoai	"	★
	Khoai Cafe	"	★

SOUTH

South Bank (SE1)

£25	Le Pont de la Tour (Bar)	Steaks & grills	(A★)
£20+	The Hartley	British, Modern	★
	The Anchor & Hope	British, Traditional	★★
	Tate Modern (Level 7)	International	A
	La Lanterna	Italian	★
	Del'Aziz	Mediterranean	(A)
	Tapas Brindisa	Spanish	-
£15+	Arch One	British, Modern	(★★)
	Butlers W'f Chop-house	British, Traditional	(A★)
	Village East	Fusion	(A★)
	Tentazioni	Italian	(★★)
	Meson don Felipe	Spanish	A
	Caffé Vergnano	Sandwiches, cakes, etc	A★
	Amano	"	★
	Amano Café	"	★
	Le Pain Quotidien	"	-
	Tas	Turkish	A
	Bangalore Express	Indian	A★
	Mango Tree	"	★
£10+	The Table	British, Modern	-
	Masters Super Fish	Fish & chips	★
	Fuzzy's Grub	Sandwiches, cakes, etc	★★
	Leon	"	-
	El Vergel	South American	★★
	Lovage	Indian	(★★)
	Inshoku	Japanese	-
£5+	Monmouth Coffee Co	Sandwiches, cakes, etc	A★★

Greenwich, Lewisham & Blackheath
(All SE postcodes, except SE1)

£20+	The Rye	International	A
	Le Querce	Italian	(★)
	Arancia	"	A
	Zero Degrees	Pizza	A
	Peninsular	Chinese	★
	Dragon Castle	"	-
	Babur Brasserie	Indian	(A★★)
	Tandoori Nights	"	A★
	Ratchada	Thai	-
£15+	The Palmerston	British, Modern	(★)
	Green & Blue	International	A
	Olley's	Fish & chips	★
	The Sea Cow	"	-
	The Gowlett	Pizza	A★
	Ganapati	Indian	A★
	Mela	"	(★)
	Everest Inn	"	-
	Thai Corner Café	Thai	★

	Thailand	"	-
£5+	The Deptford Project	*International*	-

Battersea, Brixton, Clapham, Wandsworth Barnes, Putney & Wimbledon
(All SW postcodes south of the river)

£20+	The Normanby	*British, Modern*	A★
	Phoenix	"	(★)
	Tom Ilic	"	(★)
	The Duke's Head	"	(A)
	Ma Cuisine	*French*	(★★)
	The Ship	*International*	A
	Putney Station	"	-
	Pizza Metro	*Italian*	A★★
	Buona Sera	"	A
	Rocket Riverside	*Mediterranean*	(A)
	Popeseye	*Steaks & grills*	-
	Chakalaka	*South African*	(★)
	Dalchini	*Chinese*	A★
	Kastoori	*Indian*	★★
	Mango & Silk	"	★★
£15+	Fish Club	*Fish & seafood*	★★
	Pappa Ciccia	*Italian*	A★
	Esca	"	-
	The Little Bay	*Mediterranean*	A
	Lola Rojo	*Spanish*	A★
	Rebato's	"	A★
	El Rincón Latino	"	A
	Gourmet Burger Kitchen	*Burgers, etc*	★
	Brady's	*Fish & chips*	★
	Eco	*Pizza*	★
	Boiled Egg & Soldiers	*Sandwiches, cakes, etc*	-
	China Boulevard	*Chinese*	(★)
	Chutney	*Indian*	★
	Indian Ocean	"	★
	Nazmins Balti House	"	★
	Sakonis	"	★
	Ma Goa	"	(★)
	Vijaya Krishna	*Indian, Southern*	-
	Fujiyama	*Japanese*	
	Hare & Tortoise	*Pan-Asian*	★
	The Banana Leaf Canteen	"	-
	Amaranth	*Thai*	A★★
	Ekachai	"	★
	Talad Thai	"	★
	Thai Garden	"	-
	The Paddyfield	*Vietnamese*	★★
£10+	Trinity Stores	*Italian*	A
	Fish in a Tie	*Mediterranean*	(A)
	Franco Manca	*Pizza*	★★
	Gem & I	*Turkish*	A★
	Mirch Masala SW16	*Indian*	★★
	Sree Krishna	"	★★

	Nanglo	"	A★
	The Pepper Tree	Thai	A
£5+	Hot Stuff	Indian	A★★

Outer western suburbs
Kew, Richmond, Twickenham, Teddington

£20+	Ma Cuisine	French	(★★)
	La Buvette	"	★
	Brula	"	(★)
	don Fernando's	Spanish	A
	O'Zon	Chinese	-
	Tangawizi	Indian	★
£15+	Chez Lindsay	French	(A★)
£10+	Sagar	Indian	★★

EAST

Smithfield & Farringdon (EC1)

£20+	The Quality Chop House	British, Traditional	★
	St John	"	(★)
	Cock Tavern	"	-
	The Passage Café	French	★★
	Alba	Italian	(★)
	The Eagle	Mediterranean	★
	Carnevale	Vegetarian	(★)
	Pham Sushi	Japanese	★★
	Tajima Tei	"	★
	54 Farringdon Road	Malaysian	(★)
	Cây Tre	Vietnamese	★
£15+	Smiths (Ground Floor)	British, Modern	(𝔸)
	Ambassador	"	-
	Fish Central	Fish & seafood	★
	Kolossi Grill	Greek	-
	La Porchetta Pizzeria	Italian	-
	The Little Bay	Mediterranean	𝔸
	Potemkin	Russian	-
	Moro	Spanish	(𝔸★★)
	Pinchito	"	★
	Tas	Turkish	𝔸
£10+	Kipferl	East & Cent. European	-
	Spianata & Co	Sandwiches, cakes, etc	★
	Pho	Vietnamese	𝔸★

The City (EC2, EC3, EC4)

£20+	The Fox	British, Modern	(𝔸★)
	Rocket	Mediterranean	(𝔸)
	Haz	Turkish	-
	Kasturi	Indian	-
	Kurumaya	Japanese	★
£15+	Hilliard	British, Modern	𝔸★★
	Club Mangia	"	𝔸
	Simpson's Tavern	British, Traditional	𝔸
	Gourmet Burger Kitchen	Burgers, etc	★
	Paul	Sandwiches, cakes, etc	★
	Kazan	Turkish	-
	K10	Japanese	★
	Tokyo City	"	★
	Chi Noodle & Wine Bar	Pan-Asian	𝔸
	Ekachai	Thai	★
£10+	Pure California	American	-
	Sweetings	Fish & seafood	(𝔸)
	The Place Below	Vegetarian	𝔸★
	Fuzzy's Grub	Sandwiches, cakes, etc	★★
	Spianata & Co	"	★
	Crussh	"	-
	Leon	"	-
	Chop'd	Salads	★

	Salade	"	-
£5+	Apostrophe	Sandwiches, cakes, etc	★
	Konditor & Cook	"	★

East End & Docklands (All E postcodes)

£25	Il Bordello	Italian	(Ⓐ★)
£20+	St John Bread & Wine	British, Traditional	★★
	Story Deli	Organic	Ⓐ★
	El Faro	Spanish	(★★)
	Faulkner's	Fish & chips	★★
	Albion	Ice cream	Ⓐ★
	Haz	Turkish	-
	Shanghai	Chinese	Ⓐ★
	Royal China	"	(★)
	The Drunken Monkey	"	Ⓐ
£15+	Yi-Ban	"	(★)
	Clifton	Indian	★
	Memsaheb on Thames	"	★
	The Gaylord	"	-
	Itsu	Japanese	★
	Lahore Kebab House	Pakistani	★★
	Rosa's	Thai	-
	Sông Quê	Vietnamese	★★
	Namo	"	Ⓐ★
£10+	Square Pie Company	British, Traditional	-
	Stringray Globe Café	Italian	★
	E Pellicci	"	Ⓐ
	Spianata & Co	Sandwiches, cakes, etc	★
	Crussh	"	-
	Leon	"	-
	Chop'd	Salads	★
	Mangal Ocakbasi	Turkish	★★
	Mirch Masala	Indian	★★
	New Tayyabs	Pakistani	★★
£1+	Brick Lane Beigel Bake	Sandwiches, cakes, etc	★★

MAPS

MAP I – LONDON OVERVIEW

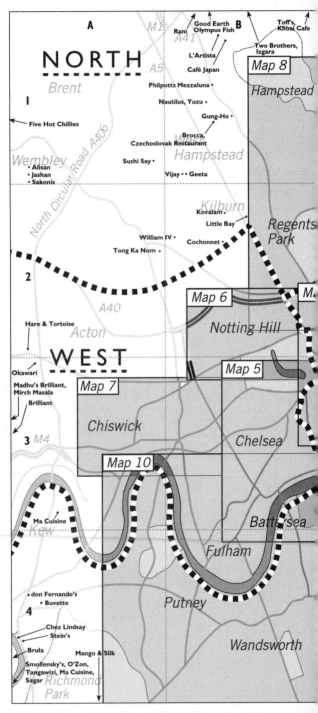

MAP 1 – LONDON OVERVIEW

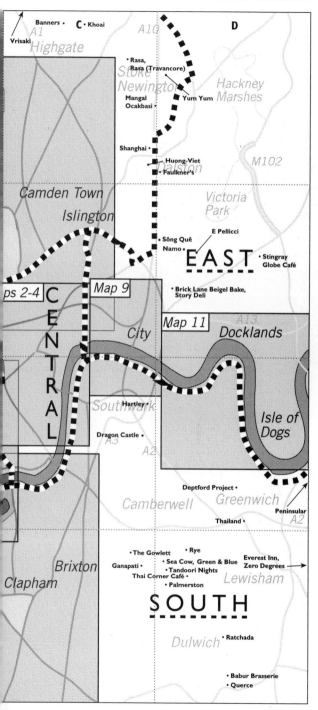

Vrisaki

Banners • **C** • Khoai

A1

Highgate

• Rasa,
Rasa (Travancore)

*Stoke
Newington*

*Hackney
Marshes*

Mangal
Ocakbasi •

Yum Yum

Shanghai •

M102

• Huong-Viet
• Faulkner's

Dalston

*Victoria
Park*

Camden Town

Islington

• Sông Quê
Namo •

E Pellicci

E A S T

• Stingray
Globe Café

ps 2-4 **C** | Map 9 |

• Brick Lane Beigel Bake,
Story Deli

**E
N
T
R
A
L**

City

| Map 11 |

Docklands

A13

Hartley •

Southwark

A3

Dragon Castle •

A2

*Isle of
Dogs*

Deptford Project •

Greenwich

Camberwell

Thailand •

Peninsular
A2

• The Gowlett   • Rye

Ganapati •   • Sea Cow, Green & Blue
• Tandoori Nights

Everest Inn,
Zero Degrees →

Thai Corner Café •

• Palmerston

Lewisham

Brixton

S O U T H

Clapham

Dulwich • Ratchada

• Babur Brasserie
• Querce

MAP 2 – WEST END OVERVIEW

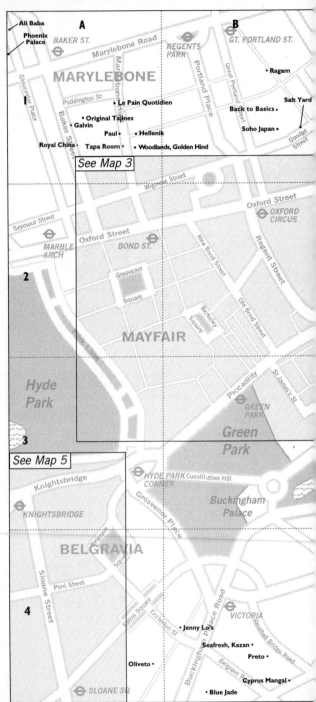

A

Ali Baba

Phoenix Palace

BAKER ST.

Marylebone Road

REGENTS PARK

B

GT. PORTLAND ST.

Portland Place

Great Portland Street

MARYLEBONE

• Ragam

Salt Yard

Paddington St

1

• Le Pain Quotidien

Back to Basics •

Gloucester Place

• Original Tajines

• Galvin

Paul •

• Hellenik

Soho Japan •

Goodge Street

Royal China •

Tapa Room •

• Woodlands, Golden Hind

Baker Street

Marylebone High Street

See Map 3

Wigmore Street

Oxford Street

OXFORD CIRCUS

Seymour Street

Oxford Street

BOND ST.

New Bond Street

Regent Street

MARBLE ARCH

2

Grosvenor Square

Berkeley Square

Old Bond Street

MAYFAIR

Hyde Park

Piccadilly

St James's St.

3

GREEN PARK

Green Park

See Map 5

Knightsbridge

HYDE PARK CORNER Constitution Hill

Grosvenor Place

KNIGHTSBRIDGE

Buckingham Palace

Sloane Street

BELGRAVIA

Pont Street

Lowndes Square

VICTORIA

Vauxhall Bridge Road

4

Eaton Square

Eccleston St

• Jenny Lo's

Buckingham Palace Road

Seafresh, Kazan •

Preto •

Belgrave Rd

Oliveto •

Cyprus Mangal •

SLOANE SQ

• Blue Jade

MAP 2 – WEST END OVERVIEW

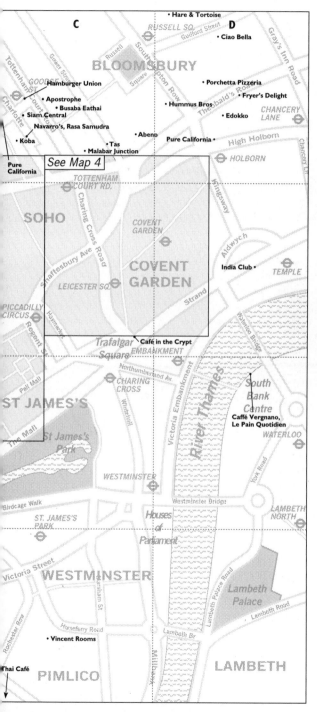

C

· Hare & Tortoise

RUSSELL SQ.

· Ciao Bella

BLOOMSBURY

D

· Hamburger Union

· Apostrophe
· Busaba Eathai

· Siam Central

Navarro's, Rasa Samudra

· Koba

· Porchetta Pizzeria
· Fryer's Delight
· Hummus Bros

· Edokko

*CHANCERY
LANE*

· Abeno

· Tas
· Malabar Junction

Pure California ·

High Holborn

Pure
California

See Map 4

TOTTENHAM
COURT RD.

SOHO

Charing Cross Road

*COVENT
GARDEN*

**COVENT
GARDEN**

India Club ·

TEMPLE

Shaftesbury Avenue

LEICESTER SQ.

Strand

*PICCADILLY
CIRCUS*

Haymarket

Regent St.

Aldwych

Café in the Crypt

*Trafalgar
Square* EMBANKMENT

ST JAMES'S

Pall Mall

Northumberland Av.

CHARING
CROSS

River Thames

Whitehall

South
Bank
Centre
Caffè Vergnano,
Le Pain Quotidien

WATERLOO

The Mall

St James's
Park

Victoria Embankment

Waterloo Bridge

WESTMINSTER

York Road

Westminster Bridge

*LAMBETH
NORTH*

Birdcage Walk

**ST. JAMES'S
PARK**

*Houses
of
Parliament*

Victoria Street

WESTMINSTER

Lambeth Palace Road

Lambeth
Palace

Lambeth Road

Rochester Row

Horseferry Road

· Vincent Rooms

Lambeth Br.

Thai Café

PIMLICO

LAMBETH

MAP 3 – MAYFAIR, ST JAMES'S & WEST SOHO

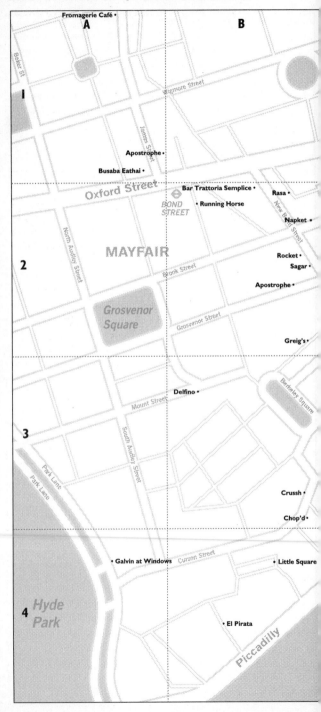

MAP 3 – MAYFAIR, ST JAMES'S & WEST SOHO

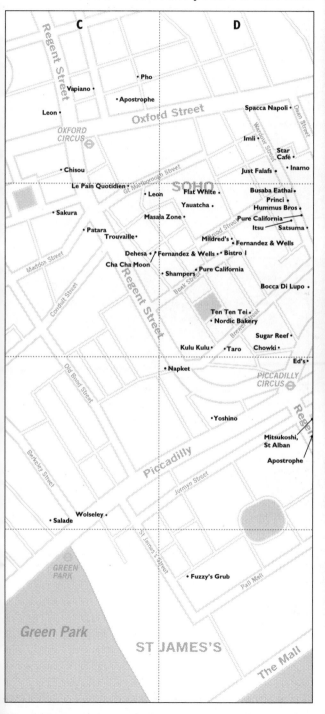

MAP 4 – EAST SOHO, CHINATOWN & COVENT GARDEN

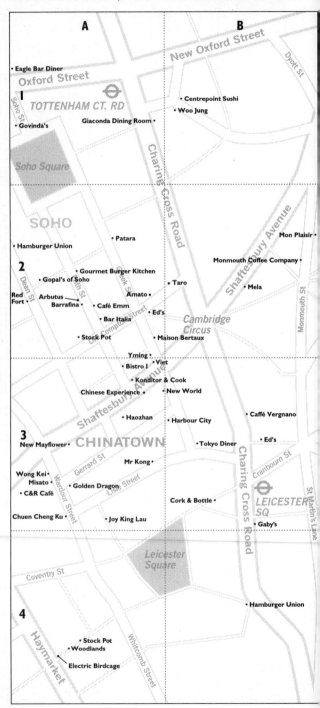

MAP 4 – EAST SOHO, CHINATOWN & COVENT GARDEN

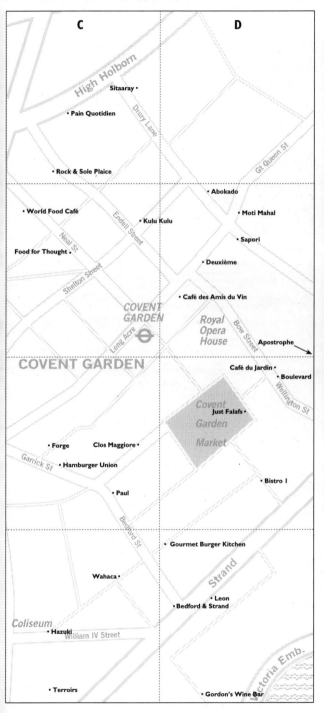

C

D

High Holborn

• Sitaaray

Drury Lane

• Pain Quotidien

Gt Queen St

• Rock & Sole Plaice

• Abokado

• World Food Café

Endell Street

• Kulu Kulu

• Moti Mahal

Neal St

• Sapori

Food for Thought •

Shelton Street

• Deuxième

• Café des Amis du Vin

COVENT GARDEN

Royal Opera House

Long Acre

Bow Street

Apostrophe →

COVENT GARDEN

Café du Jardin •

• Boulevard

Wellington St

Covent Garden Market

Just Falafs •

• Forge   Clos Maggiore •

Garrick St

• Hamburger Union

• Bistro 1

• Paul

Bedford St

• Gourmet Burger Kitchen

Strand

Wahaca •

• Leon
• Bedford & Strand

Coliseum

• Hazuki

William IV Street

Victoria Emb.

• Terroirs

• Gordon's Wine Bar

MAP 5 – KNIGHTSBRIDGE, CHELSEA & SOUTH KENSINGTON

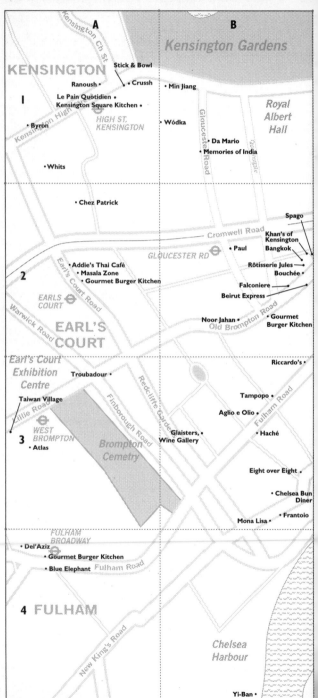

A

B

Kensington Ch St.

Kensington Gardens

KENSINGTON

Stick & Bowl

• Ranoush • Crussh

• Min Jiang

Royal Albert Hall

1

• Le Pain Quotidien
• Kensington Square Kitchen •

HIGH ST. KENSINGTON

Kensington High Road

• Wódka

• Byron

Gloucester Road

• Da Mario
• Memories of India

• Whits

• Chez Patrick

Spago •

Cromwell Road

Khan's of Kensington

GLOUCESTER RD

• Paul   Bangkok •

Rôtisserie Jules •

• Addie's Thai Café
• Masala Zone
• Gourmet Burger Kitchen

Bouchée •

Earl's Court Road

Falconiere •

Beirut Express •

2

EARLS COURT

Warwick Road

Noor Jahan •

Old Brompton Road

• Gourmet Burger Kitchen

EARL'S COURT

Earl's Court Exhibition Centre

Riccardo's •

Troubadour •

Finborough Road

Tampopo •

Taiwan Village

Redcliffe Gardens

Aglio e Olio •

Fulham Road

Lillie Road

WEST BROMPTON

Glaisters,
Wine Gallery •

• Haché

3 • Atlas

Brompton Cemetery

Eight over Eight •

• Chelsea Bun Diner

Mona Lisa •   • Frantoio

FULHAM BROADWAY

• Del'Aziz

• Gourmet Burger Kitchen

• Blue Elephant   Fulham Road

4 FULHAM

New King's Road

Chelsea Harbour

Yi-Ban •

MAP 5 – KNIGHTSBRIDGE, CHELSEA & SOUTH KENSINGTON

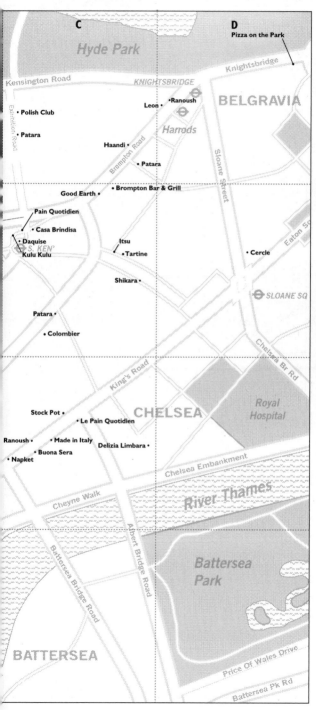

C

D

Hyde Park

Pizza on the Park

Kensington Road

Knightsbridge

KNIGHTSBRIDGE

BELGRAVIA

• Ranoush

Leon •

• Polish Club

Harrods

• Patara

Haandi •

Brompton Road

• Patara

Sloane Street

Good Earth •

• Brompton Bar & Grill

Pain Quotidien

• Casa Brindisa

Eaton Sq

• Daquise

S. KEN'

Kulu Kulu

Itsu

• Tartine

• Cercle

Shikara •

SLOANE SQ

Patara •

• Colombier

Chelsea Br Rd

King's Road

CHELSEA

Royal
Hospital

Stock Pot •

• Le Pain Quotidien

Ranoush •

• Made in Italy

Delizia Limbara •

• Buona Sera

• Napket

Chelsea Embankment

River Thames

Cheyne Walk

Albert Bridge Road

Battersea
Park

Battersea Bridge Road

BATTERSEA

Price Of Wales Drive

Battersea Pk Rd

MAP 6 – NOTTING HILL & BAYSWATER

MAP 7 – HAMMERSMITH & CHISWICK

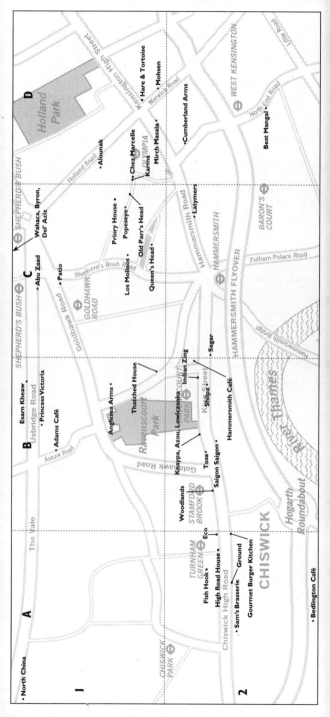

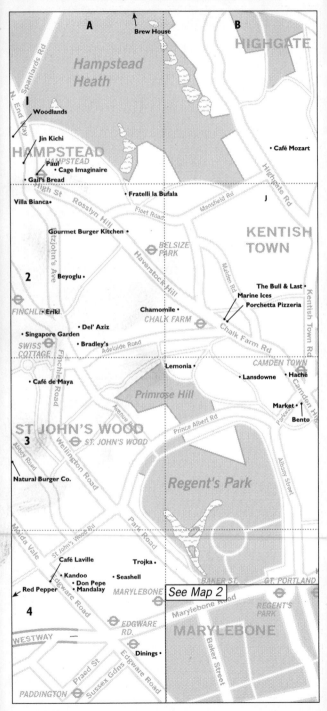

MAP 8 – HAMPSTEAD, CAMDEN TOWN & ISLINGTON

A

B

HIGHGATE

Brew House

Hampstead
Heath

N. End Way

Spaniards Rd

1

• Woodlands

• Jin Kichi

HAMPSTEAD
HAMPSTEAD

• Café Mozart

• Paul
• Cage Imaginaire
• Gail's Bread

Highgate Rd

J

High St

Rosslyn Hill

• Fratelli la Bufala

Villa Bianca •

Fleet Road

Mansfield Rd

KENTISH
TOWN

Ezzjohn's Ave

BELSIZE
PARK

Haverstock Hill

Maiden Rd

• Gourmet Burger Kitchen •

2

• Beyoglu •

FINCHLE

Finchley Road

• Eriki

• Del' Aziz

Chamomile •

CHALK FARM

The Bull & Last •

Marine Ices
Porchetta Pizzeria

Kentish Town Rd

Chalk Farm Rd

• Singapore Garden

• Bradley's

Adelaide Road

SWISS
COTTAGE

CAMDEN TOWN

Lemonia •

• Café de Maya

• Lansdowne

• Haché

Camden Hig

Primrose Hill

Market •

Avenue

Prince Albert Rd

Bento

ST JOHN'S WOOD

ST. JOHN'S WOOD

3

Wellington Road

Albany Street

Abbey Road

Natural Burger Co.

Maida Vale

Regent's Park

Park Road

St John's Wood Rd

Café Laville •

Trojka •

BAKER ST.

GT. PORTLAND

• Kandoo
• Don Pepe
• Mandalay

• Seashell

Edgware Road

MARYLEBONE

See Map 2

REGENT'S
PARK

• Red Pepper

4

EDGWARE
RD.

Marylebone Road

MARYLEBONE

WESTWAY

Praed St

Edgware Road

• Dinings

Baker Street

PADDINGTON

Sussex Gdns

MAP 8 – HAMPSTEAD, CAMDEN TOWN & ISLINGTON

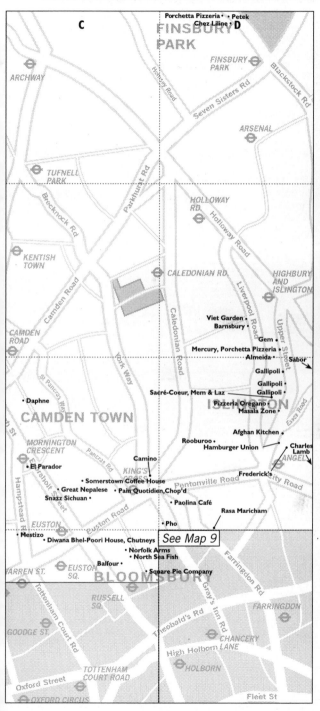

C

D

Porchetta Pizzeria • • Petek
Chez Liline •

FINSBURY
PARK

FINSBURY
PARK

ARCHWAY

Hornsey Road

Seven Sisters Rd

Blackstock Rd

ARSENAL

TUFNELL
PARK

Parkhurst Rd

Brecknock Rd

HOLLOWAY
RD.

Holloway Road

KENTISH
TOWN

CALEDONIAN RD.

Liverpool Road

HIGHBURY
AND
ISLINGTON

Camden Road

Caledonian Road

York Way

Upper Street

CAMDEN
ROAD

Viet Garden •
Barnsbury •

Gem •

Mercury, Porchetta Pizzeria •
Almeida • • •

Sabor →

Gallipoli •

Gallipoli •
Gallipoli •

• Daphne

St Pancras Way

Sacré-Coeur, Mem & Laz •

Pizzeria Oregano •
Masala Zone •

ISLINGTON

CAMDEN TOWN

MORNINGTON
CRESCENT

Pancras Rd

Afghan Kitchen •

Rooburoo •
• Hamburger Union

Charles
Lamb

Eton Road

ANGEL

• El Parador

Camino •

KING'S
CROSS

Pentonville Road

Frederick's •

City Road

Hampstead Rd

Eversholt Street

• Somerstown Coffee House
• Great Nepalese • Pain Quotidien, Chop'd
Snazz Sichuan •

Paolina Café •

Rasa Maricham •

EUSTON

Euston Road

• Pho

Mestizo •
• Diwana Bhel-Poori House, Chutneys

See Map 9

WARREN ST.

EUSTON
SQ.

Balfour •

• Norfolk Arms
• North Sea Fish

Gray's Inn Rd

Farringdon Rd

BLOOMSBURY

• Square Pie Company

RUSSELL
SQ.

FARRINGDON

GOODGE ST.

Tottenham Court Rd

Theobold's Rd

CHANCERY
LANE

High Holborn LANE

Oxford Street

TOTTENHAM
COURT ROAD

HOLBORN

OXFORD CIRCUS

Fleet St

MAP 9 – THE CITY

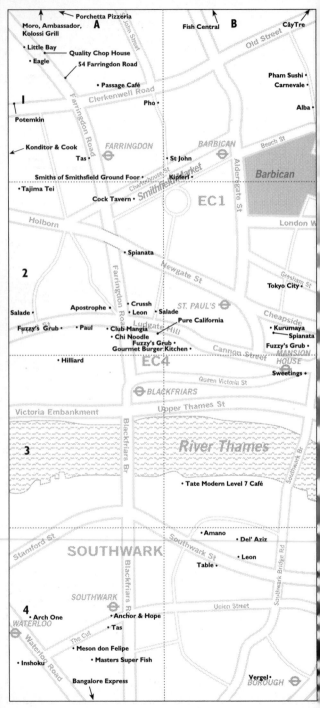

Porchetta Pizzeria

A

Fish Central

B

CâyTre

Moro, Ambassador, Kolossi Grill

• Little Bay
Quality Chop House
• Eagle
54 Farringdon Road

• Passage Café
Pho •

Pham Sushi
Carnevale

Clerkenwell Road

Alba

1

Potemkin

Konditor & Cook

FARRINGDON

BARBICAN

Beach St

Barbican

Tas •
• St John

Smiths of Smithsfield Ground Foor •
Kipferl •

EC1

London W

• Tajima Tei
Cock Tavern •

Holborn

Spianata •

Newgate St

2

Gresham St
Tokyo City •

Salade •
Apostrophe •
• Crussh
• Leon
Salade •
ST. PAUL'S
Cheapside

Fuzzy's Grub • • Paul
• Club Mangia
Pure California
• Kurumaya
Spianata

• Chi Noodle
Fuzzy's Grub •
• Fuzzy's Grub

Gourmet Burger Kitchen •
Cannon Street
MANSION HOUSE

• Hilliard

EC4

Queen Victoria St
Sweetings •

BLACKFRIARS

Upper Thames St

Victoria Embankment

River Thames

3

Blackfriars Br

Southwark Br

• Tate Modern Level 7 Café

• Amano
• Del' Aziz

SOUTHWARK

Southwark St
• Leon

Table •

SOUTHWARK

Blackfriars Rd

Union Street

Southwark Bridge Rd

4

• Arch One
• Anchor & Hope

WATERLOO
• Tas

Waterloo Road

The Cut

• Meson don Felipe

• Inshoku
• Masters Super Fish

Bangalore Express

Vergel •
BOROUGH

MAP 9 – THE CITY

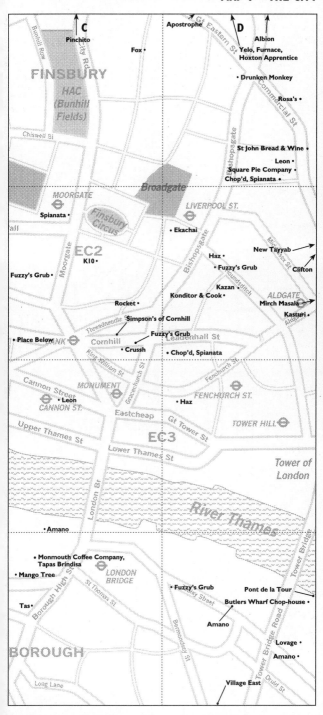

C

Pinchito

Fox

Apostrophe

D

Albion

Yelo, Furnace, Hoxton Apprentice

FINSBURY

HAC (Bunhill Fields)

Chiswell St

Drunken Monkey

Rosa's

St John Bread & Wine

Leon

Square Pie Company

Chop'd, Spianata

Broadgate

MOORGATE

Spianata

Finsbury Circus

LIVERPOOL ST.

EC2

K10

Ekachai

Haz

New Tayyab

Fuzzy's Grub

Clifton

Bishopsgate

Moorgate

Houndsditch

Kazan

ALDGATE

Fuzzy's Grub

Konditor & Cook

Mirch Masala

Rocket

Kasturi

Threadneedle St

Simpson's of Cornhill

Fuzzy's Grub

Place Below

BANK

Cornhill

Crussh

Chop'd, Spianata

King William St

Leadenhall St

Cannon St

MONUMENT

Fenchurch St

Leon

CANNON ST.

Eastcheap

Gt Tower St

Haz

FENCHURCH ST.

EC3

TOWER HILL

Upper Thames St

Lower Thames St

London Br

Tower of London

River Thames

Amano

Monmouth Coffee Company, Tapas Brindisa

LONDON BRIDGE

Mango Tree

Borough High St

St Thomas St

Fuzzy's Grub

Tooley Street

Pont de la Tour

Butlers Wharf Chop-house

Tas

Amano

Tower Bridge

Bermondsey St

Lovage

Amano

BOROUGH

Long Lane

Tower Bridge Road

Druid St

Village East

MAP 10 – SOUTH LONDON (& FULHAM)

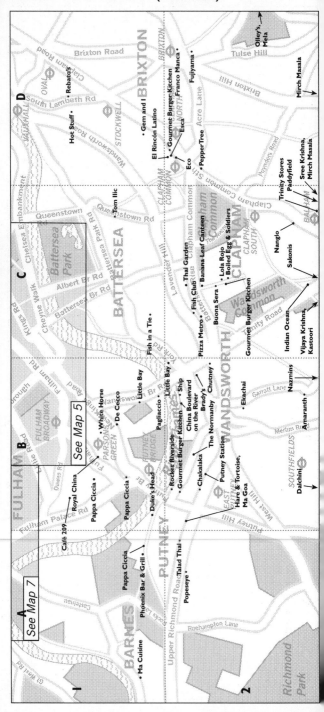

MAP 11 – EAST END & DOCKLANDS

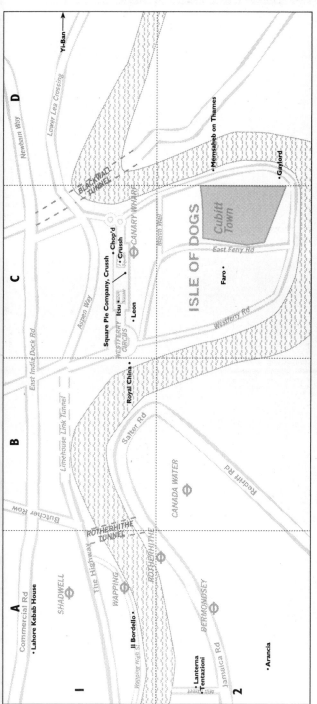

Yi-Ban

A   **B**   **C**   **D**

Commercial Rd

• Lahore Kebab House

Newham Way

Lower Lea Crossing

Butcher Row

East India Dock Rd

Aspen Way

BLACKWALL TUNNEL

Limehouse Link Tunnel

Square Pie Company, Crussh

Itsu

Leon

WESTFERRY
CIRCUS

Chop'd
Crussh

CANARY WHARF

• Memsaheb on Thames

The Highway

SHADWELL

WAPPING

Il Bordello •

Wapping High St

ROTHERHITHE
TUNNEL

ROTHERHITHE

Salter Rd

CANADA WATER

Royal China •

ISLE OF DOGS

Westferry Rd

Preston's Rd

East Ferry Rd

Cubitt Town

Faro •

• Gaylord

Lanterna
Tentazioni •

Jamaica Rd

BERMONDSEY

Redriff Rd

• Arancia

1   **2**

NOTES